ISBN 978-1-629131-05-4

Published by
Remnant Publications, Inc.
649 East Chicago Road
Coldwater, MI 49036

Text written by Bradley Booth
Copyedited by Rudy Hall, Judy Jennings, Clarissa Fiedler
Edited by Lori Peckham, Jerry Stevens
Cover design by David Berthiaume
Interior design by Eric Pletcher
Cover illustrations by Leandro Tonelli

Portions taken from the original works of E. G. White: *Patriarchs and Prophets, Prophets and Kings, The Desire of Ages, The Acts of the Apostles,* and *The Great Controversy.*

Printed in China

Children's Century
Classics
Savior of
THE
World

Table of Contents

The Son Who Left His Father

This story is taken from Luke 15.

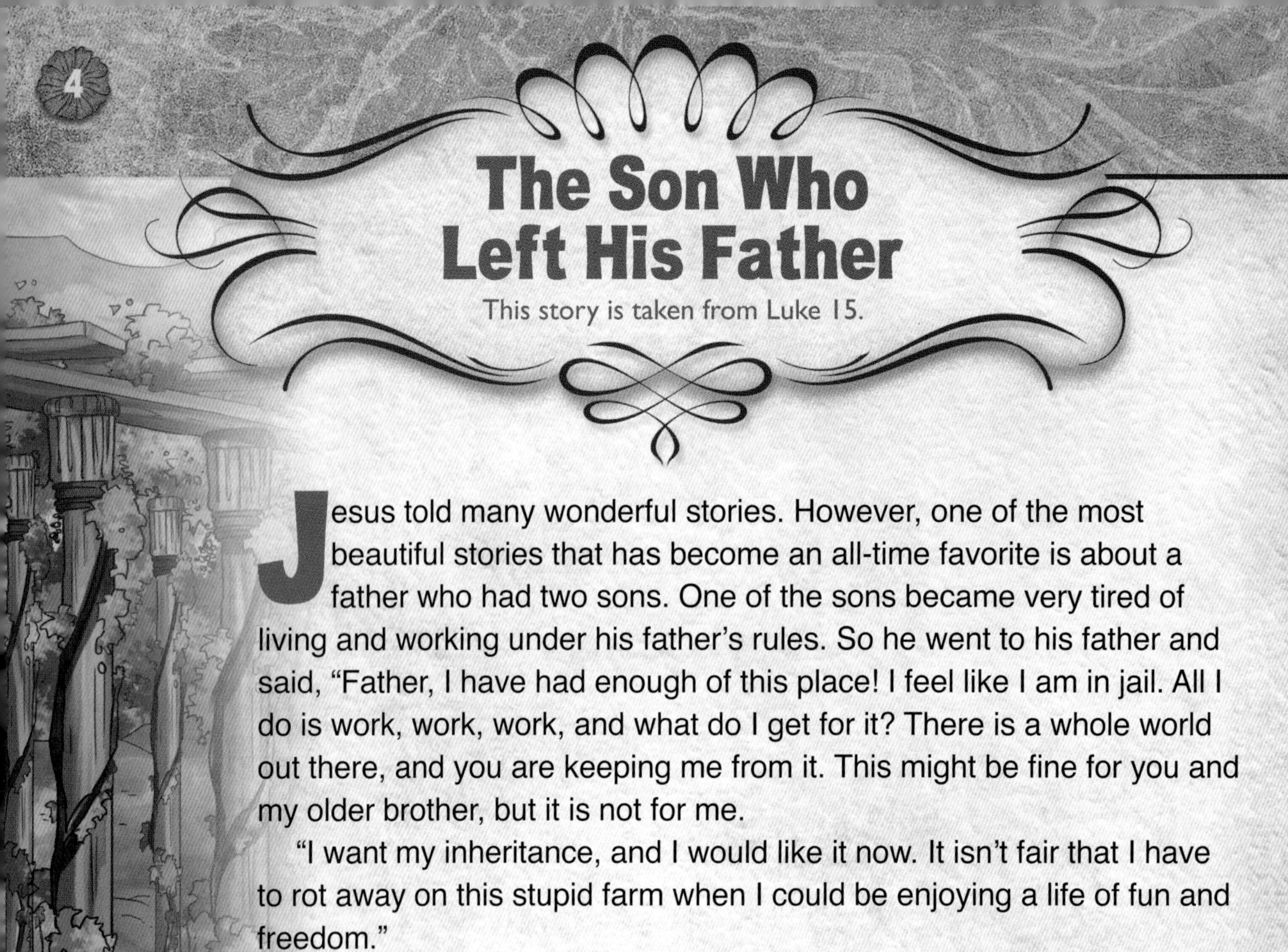

Jesus told many wonderful stories. However, one of the most beautiful stories that has become an all-time favorite is about a father who had two sons. One of the sons became very tired of living and working under his father's rules. So he went to his father and said, "Father, I have had enough of this place! I feel like I am in jail. All I do is work, work, work, and what do I get for it? There is a whole world out there, and you are keeping me from it. This might be fine for you and my older brother, but it is not for me.

"I want my inheritance, and I would like it now. It isn't fair that I have to rot away on this stupid farm when I could be enjoying a life of fun and freedom."

The father loved his son deeply and always treated him with love and fairness in every way. The son's leaving would break his heart. Yet he sadly gave his son his undeserved inheritance. He knew that leaving was a mistake on the son's part, but he would not force his son to stay with him.

The son dreamed of the day when he could be out from under his father's rules, and now it was here. So with a song in his heart and a huge smile on his face, he said "so long" to his father and brother and "hello" to a life of living as he pleased with no rules.

Making friends was easy, especially with a bag full of money. He had been told that money cannot buy friends, but it certainly did for him. He was finally free to live life just as he wanted, and so he did.

Then something happened. His bag of money got smaller and smaller until it was gone. Then his so-called friends left when the money was gone. I guess money doesn't buy real friends after all, he thought.

His thoughts were suddenly interrupted by a loud growl. It wasn't a bear or a lion. It was his stomach. He was hungry, and I mean really hungry. How would he eat with no money, no friends, and no job?

Simple, he thought. He would get a job, make money, and be back on the road to paradise in no time. The problem was there was a "severe famine in the land." That meant jobs were almost impossible to get.

By this time, he was almost starving. Finally, he got a job feeding dirty, filthy pigs. The pig food was basically garbage, but as hungry as he was it looked pretty good. He had gotten himself into quite a mess.

Feeding those filthy pigs and living like a filthy pig gave this young man some time to think and reflect on life. He thought of his two lifestyles: the life he had with his father's

The father loved his son deeply and knew that leaving was a mistake on the son's part.

way and the life he had with his own way. It didn't take him long to figure out which way was better.

Then this foolish man did a smart thing for a change. The Bible says, "He came to himself." That means he looked at his situation honestly. He decided that he had had a great life with his father, which he had foolishly traded for a life that was not fit for an animal.

Then he made a plan to get out of this terrible situation. His plan was, "I will arise and go to my father." He had absolutely nothing to take his father as a peace offering. In fact, his clothes were filthy rags. However, he would not go home empty-handed. He would take his father honesty.

He would say something like, "Father, I really messed up. I took an inheritance that I didn't deserve and lost every last dime of it. I took your love for granted and acted like a fool. I have sinned against heaven and you. I don't deserve anything, but I am humbly asking to work as a servant because I don't deserve to be treated as a son."

Then he put his sincere, heartfelt plan into action. "He arose and went to his father." He kept rehearsing his speech as he walked the long path back. Maybe his father wouldn't even see him after everything he had done, and why would he?

He knew the way back, and

Feeding those filthy pigs and living like a filthy pig gave this young man some time to think and reflect on life.

he still had a long way to go when he saw someone in the road ahead of him. It was his father! What is he doing here? he wondered. But then he saw his father running. He was running at top speed right at him. Then before he could even start his speech, his father grabbed him and kissed his neck!

For a moment he was stunned. Then he started his sincere but well-rehearsed speech. “Father, I have done a terrible sin against you. I am not worthy to be your son,” but the father wasn’t listening.

Instead, he started shouting orders to his servants: “Bring out the best robe and put it on him, and put a ring on his hand and sandals on his feet. Bring the fatted calf here, kill it, and let us eat and be merry; for this my son was dead and now is alive again; he was lost and is found.”

What a remarkable story. Sometimes we make mistakes and do some really foolish things, as this young man did. We all have a heavenly Father who loves us more than we ever know. He will not force us to love and obey Him. His love is too great for that, but if we take even one step toward Him in repentance, His arms will be around us before we know it.

After He accepts us completely, He will start giving. First, He will give us new clothes. These new clothes represent a new start. We trade in our filthy rags, which represent our sinful life, and we put on the clothes of righteousness, which only Christ can provide.

Then we will be given a feast. This feast represents extreme happiness. Any time someone makes a mistake and tells Jesus they want to return to Him, there is a big celebration in heaven.

This story represents the consequences of disobedience and the rewards of following or returning to a loving, caring Father, who only wants what is best for us.

The son had returned, and everybody was happy. Well, almost everybody.

The older brother was working when he heard all the commotion and asked one of the servants what was happening. The servant told him, "Your brother has come back home, and your father is so happy he is making a great feast for him."

His father was running at top speed right at him. Then his father grabbed him and kissed his neck!

This should have made him happy because it was his brother. Instead, he got jealous and decided not to go to the dinner to show that he wasn't very happy that his brother was back.

His father asked his son, "Why are you acting this way? Everything I have is yours, and this is your brother. I am doing the right thing by making a feast and being happy he has come back to me. My love for you has never changed, and I want you to be happy he is alive, well, and back in this family. God has told us to 'love one another as I have loved you.'"

This brother in the story forgot that. Let us never forget to obey our heavenly Father. However, if we do make a mistake, then go back. He will be waiting with open arms and a kiss on the neck. Not only will He be happy, but every angel in heaven will rejoice with Him.

Our Prayer:

"Dear Father, please keep me close to Your side. Thank You for loving me like no one else can."

Hidden Treasure Questions:

- ✔ What did the prodigal son do with the money his father gave him?
- ✔ The older brother wasn't happy to see the prodigal son come home. What did he say to the father to make his point?

Scan for bonus content

A Small Lunch and 5,000 Hungry People

This story is taken from Matthew 14, Mark 6, Luke 9, John 6 and *The Desire of Ages*, chapter 39.

It was springtime again. Bees buzzed from flower to flower on the hillsides. A soft wind was blowing. Seagulls sailed along the shore of Galilee, looking for scraps of fish the local fishermen may have left behind. The sun was already high in the sky, bringing the warmth of spring to the air.

Jesus sat with His disciples on a deserted beach of Galilee. The boat they had come in sat bobbing on the quiet waters not far from the land as the waves softly lapped at the shore. The winter months had been long, and He had been so busy with His disciples that He knew they needed a rest.

Suddenly they noticed crowds of people far away, walking along the shoreline of the lake. The disciples may have been a little upset because the crowds were always looking for them. It seemed they never had a break.

However, Jesus just smiled. "It's OK," we can hear Him saying. "If they would come this far, they must really want to be with us." Jesus could not turn away people who were hungry and thirsty for truth. These people were the very reason that He was there. He came to "seek and to save that which were lost." This multitude of people needed spiritual food, and Jesus would not turn them away.

Jesus sat with His disciples on a deserted beach of Galilee. The boat they had come in sat bobbing on the quiet waters.

Jesus welcomed everyone. He healed their sick and then began to talk. He spoke of fig trees, kings, faithful servants, and the special time in which they were living. He was a great speaker, but as usual His preaching was more like storytelling. The stories Jesus told were always interesting, and they always pointed people to the Father in heaven!

Afternoon came and went, and as the hours passed even more people arrived. Thousands arrived from up and down the coast to be with Jesus.

The people needed to go home because they had no food, but they stayed because they wanted to be with Jesus. The disciples recognized a possible problem. The people had not eaten all day, and it was late. Hungry people can be a problem, they thought, especially in a crowd of this size. So the disciples came up with a solution to fix the problem and decided to share their solution with Jesus.

"Send them away," the disciples told Jesus. They thought that if they all left, some people might get food on their way home. Anything would be better than to have all those hungry people around us, they thought. They reasoned that if the people would just go away, so would the problem.

Jesus wasn't very happy with the disciples' solution. He too had seen the thousands of very hungry people. But His mission was to draw people to Him, not to send them away from Him. Jesus had another solution for His disciples and told them, "You give them something to eat."

"For all these people?" Philip said. "Where are we going to get that kind of money? Even 200 days' wages would not be enough to feed all of these people!"

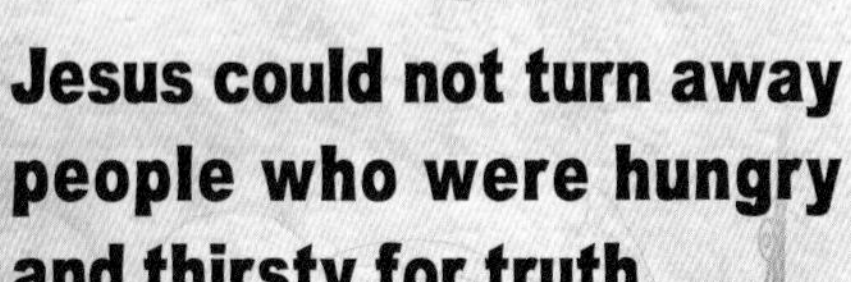

Jesus could not turn away people who were hungry and thirsty for truth.

Philip and the rest of the disciples forgot. They forgot that they were just recently sent out, and Jesus gave them power to do many wonderful miracles for the people they were sent to. They performed miracles such as casting out demons, making the blind see, healing the sick, and much more.

They also forgot that they were with a loving, caring Savior who would not send the people away in a weak and hungry condition. Jesus was just about to give the disciples a lesson on faith and compassion. He told the disciples to see if anyone in the crowd had any food to share.

They walked here and there among the people on the hillside looking for food. Finally Andrew stopped in front of small boy.

"Do you have any food that you would be willing to share?" he asked.

"Share my food?" he probably asked, smiling up at Andrew. "I guess I could. Are you hungry?"

Andrew must have grinned right back at him. "Well, yes, but it's not for me. Jesus is asking if we can find some food to feed the crowd."

"A crowd this size?" The boy would have almost laughed as he stared into his basket. "I have only got five loaves of bread and two small fish. That is not enough to feed all of these people."

"I think I would have to agree," Andrew likely admitted, "but Jesus is asking for the loaves and fish. Let's see what He does with them."

The boy agreed, and the five loaves and two fish were taken to Jesus. He had the disciples instruct the crowd to sit down in groups. Now He had the basket of food in one hand as He prayed.

When He finished asking a blessing, He reached into the basket, picked up a flat loaf of barley bread, and tore it down the middle, breaking it in two pieces. Then He tore both pieces in half again, laid the pieces in the basket, and reached for another loaf. Two barley loaves, three. Then He picked up a little fish and tore it into three or four pieces. Four

"I have only got five loaves of bread and two small fish."

barley loaves, five barley loaves. Then another fish. Six barley loaves, seven barley loaves, eight barley loaves.

The boy's eyes grew big. "Wait a minute," he thought. "Where is Jesus getting so much bread to break? And where are the fish coming from?" The basket in Jesus' lap was almost full now of broken pieces of bread and fish.

The young boy was eating some of the bread and fish now. Jesus had performed a miracle!

"How did He do that?" the boy asked himself. "I gave Jesus a little food, and now the basket is full! There is no way that little bit of bread and fish could make up a full basket, even if Jesus did break it into smaller pieces!"

Andrew and the rest of the disciples took the food from Jesus and walked up the hill, handing pieces of food to the people as they went. The people grabbed the bread and fish and ate it hungrily, thanking Andrew and the rest of the disciples with warm, grateful smiles.

The young boy was eating some of the bread and fish now too, and suddenly it hit him. Jesus had performed a miracle! A wonderful, incredible miracle! He had heard that Jesus could cast out demons! He could heal the blind! He could calm a storm, and now He had multiplied the bread and fish so much that thousands were fed! What a day this had turned out to be!

Our Prayer:

"Thank You for all the blessings of life. Please help us to be grateful for all of Your gifts, even if it is just bread and fish."

Hidden Treasure Questions:

- ✔ How many fish and loaves of bread did the little boy offer Jesus?
- ✔ Can you imagine watching Jesus perform such a miracle? How would you react if you saw such a miracle?

Listen to this story online!

Peter Walks on Water

This story is taken from Matthew 14, Mark 6, John 6, and *The Desire of Ages,* chapter 40.

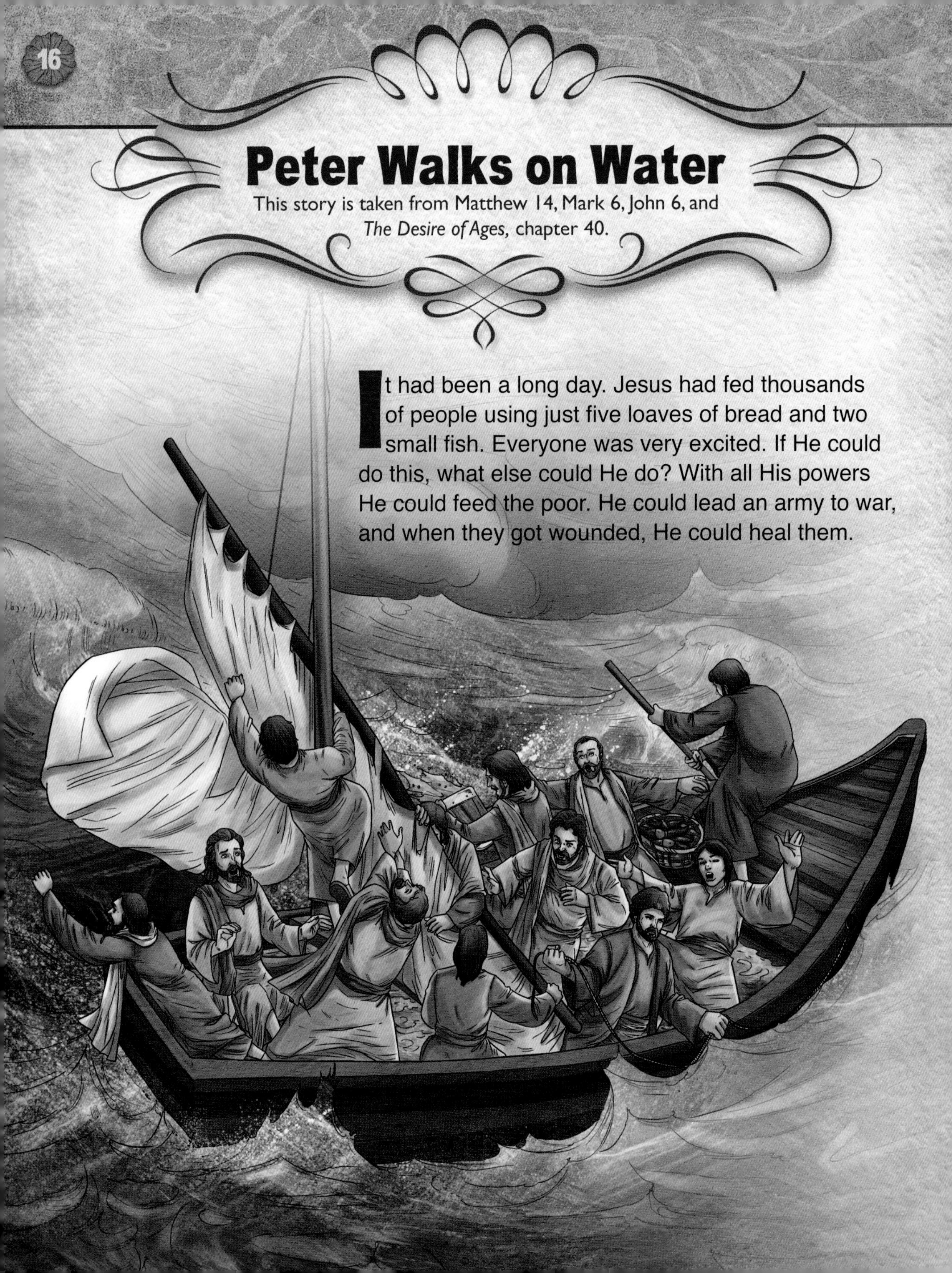

It had been a long day. Jesus had fed thousands of people using just five loaves of bread and two small fish. Everyone was very excited. If He could do this, what else could He do? With all His powers He could feed the poor. He could lead an army to war, and when they got wounded, He could heal them.

Or if they died in battle, He could even raise them to life. He was the perfect Messiah, and definitely the One they wanted to sit on the throne of Israel.

If the multitude got what they wanted, that is exactly what would have happened. They had hardly finished the loaves and fish when they decided to crown Jesus king right there on the beach. They believed that He was too humble to ever make that decision Himself, so the leaders in the crowd took charge. They would take Jesus by force if necessary, and the disciples were ready to help.

But that is not at all what Jesus had in mind. Jesus continually told the people that His kingdom was not of this world—that it was a spiritual kingdom in the heart. It was not about fighting battles with swords and shields. It was about the battle between good and evil that was going on between Satan and God. Jesus had come to die for the sins of the world, and that was His mission in this world!

The crowds didn't agree. They didn't want to hear about a spiritual or a future kingdom. They wanted a king now! However, Jesus gave them no chance to argue. Quickly He took action by telling everybody to go home. They protested, but when they heard His voice of authority and saw the stern look on His face, they realized that they had no choice. Within minutes the disappointed crowd was breaking up, and Jesus had ordered His disciples to get into their boat. They were instructed to make the return trip across the Sea of Galilee without Him, and He would catch up with them later.

They decided they had no hope and would die in this terrible storm. How they wished Jesus was with them!

With great disappointment the disciples did as they were told. This was one of the lowest points in their lives! Some of them had been with Jesus for two years now. They had seen His miracles. They had heard Him preach and teach, and they knew that the words He spoke could change their lives. But when He refused to become king when it was obvious that was what the people wanted, it was almost more than they could bear.

The disciples were discouraged and worn-out physically when Satan came to them with his biggest temptation of all. Maybe Jesus wasn't the Messiah they had been looking for, Satan whispered in their minds. Maybe He wasn't the Son of God and was just an imposter.

After everyone was gone, Jesus went up into the hills to pray and to meditate about all that had happened that day. He prayed that His disciples would understand His true mission, because until they understood that, they could not teach others.

He realized that this day had been a turning point in His ministry for the people of Galilee. The religious leaders in Judea had already rejected him, and now it looked as if the people of Galilee would do the same. Soon many of those who had been His most devoted followers would leave and not follow Him anymore. They had come for what they could get from Him, whether it was healing, loaves and fish, or just recognition because He was so popular.

Meanwhile, the disciples were out on the lake trying to get across to the western shore. They were tired and worn-out from their long day with the crowd. It had been an exciting day, but it ended with disappointment. All they could think about was how Jesus had refused to be king. Why would He turn down such an honor?

Suddenly their thoughts changed. A storm came up, and they found themselves in great danger. They forgot all about their disappointment and tried with all their might to row against the wind and waves. Hours passed, and they were losing the battle. Finally, they decided they had no hope and would die in this terrible storm. How they wished Jesus was with them!

Shortly before dawn, Jesus went out walking on the lake to encourage His disciples. How He walked on water was truly amazing, but "with God all things are possible." The same power that healed the sick, raised the dead, and made the blind see was the same power that Jesus called upon to walk on the water.

When the disciples saw Jesus walking on the lake toward them, they did not recognize Him and were terrified. "It is a ghost," they cried out in fear.

When the disciples saw Jesus walking on the water toward them, they did not recognize Him and were terrified.

Maybe they were scared because it had never occurred to them that Jesus might come walking to them on water. But also, they had turned their minds over to Satan's influence. They did this by being angry because Jesus had upset their plans of crowning Him king.

Many of the disciples were uneducated and superstitious. Although they were religious, the fear of ghosts was very real to them. The deep waters of Galilee were thought to be the home of evil spirits, which would cause storms to suddenly arise.

These disciples were tough, hardened fishermen. They didn't scare very easily, but when they saw this mysterious figure approaching them upon the waters, they were frozen with fear. They were in danger of capsizing, yet they let go of the oars and just sat there.

Jesus immediately said to them, "Don't be afraid; it is I!"

The disciples were no doubt very surprised when they heard His voice. They must have given a sigh of relief.

But Peter may have had some doubt that it was actually Jesus. Always the bold and adventuresome one, he called out, "If it's You, Lord, invite me to come out on the water."

Jesus wasted no time. "All right then, come!" He replied.

Peter got out of the boat and began walking on the water toward Jesus. What an adventure that must have been! It's likely he was showing off a bit to the other disciples too!

For a moment Peter lost sight of Jesus. He was afraid and began to sink. "Lord, save me!" he cried.

But then he heard the wind and saw the waves rise up so high that for a moment he lost sight of Jesus. He was afraid and began to sink. "Lord, save me!" he cried.

In an instant Jesus was beside him, reaching out His hand to catch him. "You have such little faith," He told Peter as they walked back to the boat. "Why did you doubt that I could keep you safe?"

When the two of them reached the boat and climbed in, the wind calmed down. The disciples were in awe that Jesus could walk on water. They knelt at His feet to worship Him. "Truly, You are the Son of God!" they said.

I am sure the disciples never forgot that night on the lake. When they needed help, Jesus was only a prayer away. Remember that you never have to deal with your problems alone. Jesus will lift you out of your problems, just like He lifted Peter out of the water. All you have to do is call on Him.

Our Prayer:

"Dear Jesus, thank You for always keeping me safe. I don't ever need to be afraid when I am with You."

Hidden Treasure Questions:

- ✔ Why did Jesus send all the people away after He had fed them miraculously with bread and fish?
- ✔ When the disciples saw Jesus walking on the water, what did they say?

Listen to this story online!

Scan for bonus content

A Mother's Great Faith Saves Her Daughter

This story is taken from Matthew 15, Mark 7, and *The Desire of Ages,* chapter 43.

The Pharisees and scribes in Capernaum did not like Jesus. He taught from the Scriptures and not the traditions of the Jewish Sanhedrin as they did, so they had many disagreements.

When crowds of people would gather around Jesus to listen to His words from Scripture, the Pharisees would try to argue with Him. This made things very difficult for Jesus. He realized that this was not the best place to spread the gospel right now and decided to leave Galilee for a while.

The Pharisees wanted to kill Jesus, but it was not time for Him to die yet. He still needed to do many things to fulfill His mission in this world.

There were more lessons for the disciples to learn, so Jesus decided to take them on a trip into the hill country of Phoenicia. The area they were going to visit was full of history. The Phoenicians were excellent sailors and had become some of the world's richest traders. They had built magnificent temples and palaces. They had been close friends with King David and his son Solomon.

The disciples had never been to a foreign country before. They had traveled with Jesus to many places and seen Him help many kinds of people who were not Jews. He had preached to Samaritans. He had healed a Roman centurion's servant. He had cast demons out of pagan demoniacs on the eastern shore of Lake Galilee, but all of those people lived among the Jews.

Going to another country was a completely different experience for the disciples. However, Jesus had come to Phoenicia for a very special reason. He wanted to teach His disciples a valuable lesson in Christian kindness.

One day, as He and His disciples were walking, a Phoenician woman came out on the road and began following Jesus.

"Have mercy on me, O Lord, Son of David!" she called. "My daughter is possessed by a devil and is suffering terribly!"

"Have mercy on me, O Lord, Son of David!" she called. "My daughter is possessed by a devil and is suffering."

This Phoenician mother had tried to get help for her daughter from her heathen gods, but she always came away disappointed. They could do nothing for her because, of course, these gods were only pieces of stone, wood, or metal.

She had heard of Jesus and His miracles from some of the Jews who lived in her city. The stories they told said that He could heal any disease, and she was determined that if He ever came her way, she would ask Him to heal her daughter.

Sometimes in her discouragement she would ask herself, "Why would a Jewish rabbi do this for us?" Then she would remember that people said He accepted everyone, and hope would again spring in her heart. Jesus was her only chance if she ever wanted her daughter to be normal again.

Now she had her chance. The Miracle Man Himself had come to the area where she lived.

"Have mercy on me, O Lord, Son of David!" she kept calling as she continued to follow Jesus down the road.

Jesus did not answer the woman right way, and His disciples finally asked Him to send her away. "She is annoying us!" they said.

Jesus turned to the woman. "I was sent only to the lost sheep of Israel," He replied. In other words, "I came to help the Jews, not you."

That does not sound very nice, and we can hardly imagine why Jesus would say such a thing! However, Jesus wanted to teach His disciples a lesson in an unusual way about how to treat people.

Jesus looked at the woman kindly. "It is not good to take the children's bread and throw it to the little dogs," He said.

Now, we would think that Jesus' words would hurt the woman's feelings and discourage her, but that is not what happened. Instead, the woman came and knelt before Him. "Lord, please help me!" she begged.

Jesus looked at the woman kindly. "It is not good to take the children's bread and throw it to the little dogs," He said.

"That's right, Lord," came her quick reply, "yet even the little dogs eat the crumbs that fall from their masters' table."

Jesus was very impressed. "Woman, you have great faith! You may go home now, because your prayer has been heard."

And clearly, it had. The woman went home and found that her daughter had been set free from the demon at the very moment that Jesus had given the command.

What did God want the disciples to learn? That Jesus wants us to be kind to everyone, even if they are not from our country, church, or culture. He loves everyone the same and will help anyone who needs Him.

Our Prayer:

"Dear Jesus, help me to be kind to everyone, even if they are different from me."

Hidden Treasure Questions:

- What country did Jesus and His disciples go to on a road trip?
- What did the woman ask Jesus to do for her daughter?

Listen to this story online!

Scan for bonus content

An Unforgettable Night

This story is taken from Matthew 16 and 17, Mark 9, Luke 9, and *The Desire of Ages*, chapter 46.

Jesus knew that it wasn't long before He must go to Jerusalem for the last time. The chief priests and temple teachers didn't like Him. In fact, they were planning how they could capture Him and kill Him. Many times, He tried to tell the disciples that He would soon die a horrible death by crucifixion and be raised the third day, but they did not want to hear Him talking about such things.

One day Peter finally took Him aside and scolded Him, "Lord, don't say things like that! We are never going to let something like that happen to You!"

Jesus knew that Peter meant well, but He also understood that Satan was using Peter to discourage Him. "Get behind Me, Satan!" Jesus said, looking at Peter. "You are a stumbling block to Me! You are not worried about what God wants as much as you are about what you want!"

Of course, Jesus did not mean Peter was Satan. It was just that He could see that Peter was speaking more for Satan than he was for God.

Then He turned to all the disciples to make His point. "Things are not as they seem," He said sadly. "Soon I am going to suffer many things in Jerusalem, and so are you. From now on whoever wants to be My disciple must be ready to deny himself and take up his cross to follow Me. Those who are more worried about saving their lives in this world are more likely to lose them eternally."

One evening Jesus called Peter, James, and John to His side. He had a very important trip planned. He was going up a mountain to a secluded place to pray, but that wasn't all. Something very special was about to happen, and it was important that Peter, James, and John were there.

All the disciples were important to Jesus, but Peter, James, and John were closer to Him and were almost constantly with Him.

Jesus left Peter, James, and John by themselves at some point on the mountain and went a little farther to pray alone. The disciples soon fell asleep, but Jesus prayed on into the night.

He knew that difficult trials were coming for Him and His disciples in Jerusalem. He also knew that His disciples would almost lose their faith in Him during this great time of trial. Therefore, He prayed to His Father, asking Him to show them a sign from heaven. “Help them see that I am the Messiah and the Savior of the world,” He said.

While Jesus was kneeling in prayer, the gates of heaven suddenly opened and God’s glory shone upon Him. His face glowed like the sun, and His clothes became as white as snow.

The three disciples awoke suddenly from their sleep to see Jesus in all His glory, but they also noticed two heavenly visitors standing with Him on the mountain. These men were some of the most famous men in all of Hebrew history.

One was Moses, who had led the Israelites from Egypt into the Promised Land more than 1,400 years before. He had died before reaching Canaan, but then had been raised to life by God and taken to heaven.

The other visitor was the prophet Elijah. He had preached and prophesied warning messages against the northern tribes of Israel 800 years earlier because of their great wickedness. Then God

"Get behind Me, Satan!" Jesus said, looking at Peter. "You are a stumbling block to Me!"

had rewarded him by taking him to heaven in a chariot of fire without having to die.

Moses and Elijah came to encourage Jesus, but they also represented two groups of God's people down through the ages. Moses represented all those who were faithful, but who died here on earth. Elijah represented those who will live to see Jesus come the second time, and who will be taken to heaven without having to die.

Moses and Elijah came to encourage Jesus, but they also represented two groups of God's people down through the ages.

The disciples were overwhelmed by the glorious scene before them! They were wondering what would happen next when suddenly they heard a voice from heaven saying, "This is My Son whom I have chosen, and I am very pleased with Him. Listen to what He has to say!"

When the disciples heard the awesome voice, they were afraid, fell on the ground, and covered their faces. They did not move until Jesus came and touched them. "Get up," He said. "Do not be afraid. We are alone now."

What an experience that had been! Months later, after Jesus had been resurrected and gone back to heaven, the disciples would remember that night. The memory of the experience would encourage them to be faithful. They had seen Jesus in all His heavenly glory, and someday soon He would come again, and look just like that.

Our Prayer:

"Dear Jesus, I cannot wait to see You in Your robe of light as the disciples saw You that night on the mountain."

Hidden Treasure Questions:

- ✔ How many disciples went with Jesus up on the mountain to pray?
- ✔ Who came from heaven to visit Jesus when He was on the mountain?

Listen to this story online!

Scan for bonus content

Demon-Possessed Boy

This story is taken from Matthew 17, Mark 9, Luke 9, and *The Desire of Ages*, chapter 47.

Peter, James, and John had spent the night with Jesus on the mountain praying. They had also been witnesses to an incredible appearance by Moses and Elijah from heaven to encourage Jesus. Most awesome of all was the voice they had heard from heaven telling them that Jesus was the Son of God. It was an amazing memory that they would have for the rest of their lives!

Now it was time to come down off the mountain and continue their ministry with Jesus as He healed and preached in Galilee. As they reached the foot of the mountain, they spotted the rest of the disciples. A large crowd had surrounded them, and some Jewish scribes were arguing with them.

However, as soon as the people in the crowd saw Jesus, they all ran to greet Him.

"What are you arguing about?" Jesus asked them.

A man in the crowd who had his son with him replied, "Teacher, my son is possessed by a spirit that won't let him speak. Sometimes when it seizes him and throws him to the ground, he foams at the mouth, grinds his teeth, and becomes stiff like a dead man. I asked Your disciples to drive out the spirit, but they could not."

Jesus was very disappointed with His disciples! "How long must I wait for you to grow in faith?" He sighed. "What a group of unbelievers you've turned out to be! Bring Me the boy."

They brought the boy, and then a horrible battle began! When the spirit saw Jesus, it immediately threw the boy to the ground in a convulsion. He thrashed around moaning and groaning, and his eyes looked wild as though he was a crazy animal. It was a scary sight to see the boy in such pain.

A man in the crowd who had his son with him replied, "Teacher, my son is possessed by a spirit."

Jesus asked the boy's father, "How long has he been like this?"

"Since he was just a little boy," the

father replied. “It has often thrown him in the fire to burn him and sometimes in water to drown him.” The father grabbed the sleeve of Jesus’ robe. “If You can do anything, please take pity on us and help us!”

“‘If I can?” Jesus asked in surprise. “If you can believe, all things are possible to him who believes.”

The father stared at Jesus, and then suddenly grew frightened as he realized what Jesus was saying. Was it possible that his only chance of getting help for his boy was slipping away? This was Jesus, a Miracle Worker with powers from heaven! People said He could cure any kind of disease, and now maybe the father’s own lack of faith was going to keep Jesus from helping his boy.

Immediately the father exclaimed, “I do believe! I do!” But then he slowly sank to his knees at Jesus’ feet, realizing how weak his faith must look to Jesus. “Help me overcome my unbelief!” he cried with tears in his eyes.

When Jesus saw that an even bigger crowd was gathering to see what was happening at the scene, He decided not to wait any longer.

"Deaf and dumb spirit," He said, "I command you, come out of him and enter him no more!"

The spirit shrieked, shook the boy violently, and then finally came out of him. Now the boy lay very still. In fact, it looked like the demon might have killed him. "He's dead," the crowd whispered among themselves.

The spirit shrieked, shook the boy violently, and then finally came out of him.

But Jesus took the boy by the hand and lifted him up on his feet. The boy looked calm. His eyes were clear, and he wasn't shaking anymore.

"Thank You! Thank You!" the father cried again and again as he fell at Jesus' feet to worship Him. "My son is well now! Praise God, my son is well!"

Later when Jesus and His disciples had gone to the home of a friend, the disciples spoke to Him privately. "What did we do wrong, Master?" they asked. "Why couldn't we drive the demon out?"

Jesus shook His head and sadly told them, "This kind of demon can come out only by much prayer and fasting. If you had even the smallest amount of genuine faith, you could have done this. I'm serious! Even if your faith is no bigger than a grain of mustard seed, you can move mountains! Nothing will be impossible for you!"

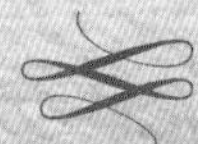

Our Prayer:

"Dear Jesus, help me to have faith when I need it most."

Hidden Treasure Questions:

- ✔ What were the people in the crowd arguing about when Jesus and the three disciples came down off the mountain?
- ✔ What did the father say when he realized that Jesus might not heal his son?

Listen to this story online!

Scan for bonus content

Money in a Fish's Mouth

This story is taken from Matthew 17 and *The Desire of Ages*, chapter 48.

One day an officer from the temple in Jerusalem stopped Peter in the streets of Capernaum. "Does your Teacher not pay the temple tax?" he asked. In those days every man in Israel was supposed to pay a yearly tax to support the temple building program. It wasn't really a tax, but more like an offering.

Peter didn't want Jesus to get into trouble. He believed that Jesus was the Messiah and the most wonderful Person in the world! However, he did not want the officer to think that Jesus wasn't loyal to God, or that He was unwilling to support the temple. Jesus was the most amazing Man he and the other disciples had ever met, and he wanted everyone else to think so, too!

Peter was right to be careful. The scribes and Pharisees were always looking for an excuse to make trouble for Jesus. They had sent this temple officer especially to ask the trick question. According to the Scriptures, they knew that the priests and prophets were not required to pay the tax. If Jesus told them that He didn't pay the tax, all of His followers might question His love for God and the temple services in Jerusalem. If He said He did pay the tax, He would be admitting that He was not a prophet and definitely not the Messiah.

The scribes and Pharisees hoped that tricking Jesus in this way would prove to everyone that Jesus was, in fact, not the Messiah they were looking for!

But Peter was not thinking about any of that. So when the tax officer asked Peter, "Does Jesus pay the temple tax?" Peter quickly answered, "Yes, of course."

He should have taken the time to ask Jesus about it. Now some might doubt that Jesus was the Messiah or think that He didn't know the Scriptures. After all, if He knew the Scriptures, He would know that Moses had said He didn't have to pay the tax.

A few days before this Jesus had asked His disciples, "Who is everyone saying that I am?"

The disciples knew that many people were calling Him John the Baptist, whom some thought had been raised from the dead. Some people were saying He was Elijah and others Jeremiah.

"But who do you say that I am?" Jesus asked, wanting to know how the disciples felt personally.

Peter, always ready to say what was on his mind, was the first to answer. "You are the Christ, the Son of the living God!" he said.

An officer from the temple in Jerusalem stopped Peter in the streets of Capernaum. "Does your Teacher not pay the temple tax?"

This answer showed Jesus that His disciples could understand things that many others could not. However, now the temple officer was trying to put doubt in Peter's mind as to whether or not Jesus was the Messiah after all.

Jesus knew that the officer had asked Peter for a temple tax, and so later when

Peter did as Jesus had asked, and there was a coin in the first fish he caught, just as Jesus said.

He was resting with His disciples, He asked Peter, "What do you think, Peter? From whom do the kings of the earth collect taxes? From their sons or from strangers?"

"Strangers, of course," Peter replied.

"Then the sons are free," Jesus said.

Jesus was the Son of God. He had been the One to whom all of the services in the temple pointed. Like the priests and prophets, He was free from having to pay the tax.

"However, we do not want to offend anyone," Jesus said, "so this is what I would like you to do. Go to the lake, throw in a hook, and take the first fish that comes up on your line. Then open its mouth, and you will find a coin inside. Take that money and give it to the temple officer to pay the tax for you and Me."

Peter did as Jesus had asked, and there was a coin in the first fish he caught, just as Jesus had told him there would be!

This was a miracle of the most unusual kind. In performing it, Jesus helped Peter see who He really was. He was the Messiah, the Son of God, and He should not have to pay the temple tax. He was the Creator of all things. He owned the cattle on a thousand hills and all the fish in the sea.

Our Prayer:

"Dear Father in heaven, help me to obey the laws of my city and country as much as possible, as long as they do not ask me to be unfaithful to You."

Hidden Treasure Questions:

- ✔ What did the temple officer ask Peter one day on the street?
- ✔ What miracle did Jesus perform to prove to Peter that He was the Messiah and the Son of God?

Blind Man Healed

This story is taken from John 9 and *The Desire of Ages*, chapter 51.

One Sabbath Jesus and His disciples were visiting the temple in Jerusalem, as they often did on Jewish feast days. All kinds of people were at the temple that day. Some came to offer sacrifices, and some came to give offerings and pray. However, some came because they needed to beg for food or money.

As Jesus walked through the court of the temple, He noticed a blind man sitting on the stone pavement begging.

Jesus' disciples saw the man too. "Whose fault is it that this man is blind?" they asked Jesus. "Is the man being punished because he sinned, or because his parents sinned?"

"Neither this man nor his parents sinned," Jesus replied, "but that God's name might be proclaimed here in Jerusalem. God wants to show His love through healing the ones who need Him most.

"That is what we are supposed to do every day," Jesus added. "While times are good, we must do what we can to show everyone how much My Father loves them. Unfortunately, the days are coming when none of us will be able to do that.

"I am the light of the world," He said as He squatted on the ground and scooped up some clay dirt in His hand. Then He did a very strange thing. He spit on the clay in His hand, mixed it all together, and rubbed some of it on the blind man's eyelids.

"Go wash your eyes in the pool of Siloam," He told the blind man.

The blind man obeyed and went to the pool of Siloam to wash his eyes, and immediately he was healed. It was a miracle! We can imagine how excited he must have been as he praised God for heaven's gift of healing. He had obeyed Jesus, and God had rewarded him for his faith.

Everyone who knew the blind man was shocked! "Isn't this the man who has been begging here at the temple for years?" they asked in amazement.

"It can't be!" others said. "How can a man who was as blind as that be healed? It is impossible! How did this happen?" they asked the man.

As Jesus walked through the court of the temple, He noticed a blind man sitting on the stone pavement.

"A Man called Jesus made clay and anointed my eyes. Then He told me to go wash in the pool of Siloam," said the man who had been blind. "So I went and washed, and now I can see."

The Pharisees called in the blind man again. "Tell us, how do you think it is possible that Jesus could have healed you?"

The crowds were beginning to gather to see what all the commotion was about, and they took the man to see the temple elders.

The Pharisees asked him how he had received his sight, and he told them the same thing that he had told the others: "A Man called Jesus gave me my sight."

The Pharisees were very upset that Jesus had healed the blind man on the Sabbath, so they called a private meeting to talk about it. "Whoever did this cannot be a Man of God," they said, "because He doesn't keep the Sabbath day holy."

"Maybe not," others argued, "but how can a man who is a sinner do such miracles?"

There was a division among the leaders because they could not agree on where Jesus received the power to heal the blind man.

The Pharisees called in the blind man again. “”Tell us, how do you think it is possible that Jesus could have healed you?” they said.

“I think He is a prophet,” the man replied.

But the Pharisees continued to argue among themselves. “Are we really sure this man was blind?” they said.

It was such a shame to hear them saying such things! God had given them a marvelous sign that Jesus was indeed the Messiah and the Son of God, and still they refused to believe!

Next, the Pharisees called in the parents of the man. “Is this your son, whom you say was born blind?” they asked. “And if so, how is it possible he can now see?”

The mother and father were very careful how they answered the religious leaders. They had heard that anyone who claimed that Jesus was the Messiah would no longer be allowed to worship in the temple.

“We know this is our son, and that he was born blind,” they said, “but we have no idea how he can see now, and we don’t know the Man he claims healed him. Our son is old enough to speak for himself. Ask him.”

Once again, the Pharisees called in the man who had been healed. They still had no explanation for the healing, and this made them angry. “Tell us that the Man who healed you is a sinner, and we will forget the whole thing!” they ordered him.

“Maybe He is a sinner, and maybe He is not. I don’t know,” replied the man, “but one thing I do know. I was blind before, and now I can see.”

“But what did He do exactly?” they asked. “How did He open your eyes?

“I have told you already, and you do not believe me,” the man said in surprise. “Why are you asking me again? Do you want to become His disciples too?”

This really made the Pharisees angry. “You may be His disciple, but we are not!” they exclaimed. “We know that God spoke through Moses, and we are his disciples. As for this Man Jesus, we have no idea where He came from!”

The man healed of his blindness was surprised at their unbelief. “This is amazing!” he said. “You say you don’t know where Jesus is from, or whether He is a sinner, and yet He opened my eyes! In this world, such a thing is not possible! If this Jesus were not a Man of God, He would not have the power to do such a thing!"

The Pharisees were so upset by now that they would no longer listen to the man who had been blind. "You are a sinner yourself, and you would teach us?" they shouted as they ordered the guards to throw him out of the temple.

When Jesus heard that the Pharisees had thrown the man out of the temple, He went to find him.

When Jesus heard that the Pharisees had thrown the man out of the temple, He went to find him in the outer court. "Do you believe in the Son of God?" Jesus asked.

"Who is He that I may believe in Him?" the man asked.

"You have already seen Him," Jesus replied. "It is He who is talking to you."

The man fell to his knees to worship Jesus. "I believe," he said reverently.

Jesus was very sad that the Pharisees found it so hard to believe He was the Messiah. Even though they had seen proof in the miracles that He had performed, they still refused to believe. They might not have been physically blind, but because of their unbelief, they were spiritually blind, and that made them greater sinners than anyone else.

Our Prayer:

"Dear Jesus, help me to believe when I see Your power working in my life."

Hidden Treasure Questions:

- What did Jesus do to heal the blind man?
- What did the parents say to the Pharisees when asked how it was possible for Jesus to heal their son?

The Lost Sheep

This story is taken from Matthew 18, Luke 15, and *The Desire of Ages*, chapter 52.

Jesus' time on earth was almost finished, and He knew there were still so many people in Israel who were lost. They did not understand that God loved them so much that He would send His only Son to die for them.

Jesus was the most popular rabbi in all Israel. Most of the religious leaders in Judea and Galilee had rejected Him as the Messiah, but the Gentiles and pagans loved Him. They flocked to wherever Jesus was to see Him preach and heal, especially the tax collectors and sinners.

This made the scribes and Pharisees angry. They hated the tax collectors and sinners who followed Jesus everywhere, and they despised Jesus for His friendship with them. However, they were also jealous of Jesus because He was so popular that thousands in Israel wanted to be with Him all the time.

So the good shepherd left his 99 sheep in the care of a servant and went out to find that one lost sheep.

"This man welcomes sinners and eats with them," the Pharisees and teachers of the law muttered one day as they watched Jesus eating with people whom they would have nothing to do with.

Jesus knew what these religious leaders were thinking, so He decided to tell them a parable about a lost sheep.

There once was a man who had 100 sheep. One evening when he came home, he counted the sheep and discovered that one was missing. Where had the sheep gone astray? he wondered. But he had no idea. It could be anywhere. However, he needed to find the sheep, and if he was going to do that, he needed to do it quickly before darkness fell. The hour was late.

So he left his 99 sheep in the care of a servant and went out to find that one lost sheep. It was getting colder now, and a sharp wind had come up. As he retraced his steps from that day, he looked for signs of the lost sheep. Thorns cut through his sandals as he climbed a rocky pathway over a mountain pass. By now it was growing dark, and he had to light a torch as he picked his way through a narrow canyon.

He had been many places that day with his flock. Where could that lost sheep be? Was he already too late? Had a wild beast hunted down the poor sheep and killed it?

Then to his great excitement, he heard the call of his sheep faint and weak somewhere in the darkness. But it was still alive. When he finally found it caught on the side of the cliff, it was so weak that it could not even walk. So he put it on his shoulders and carried it home.

With great rejoicing, he called his friends and neighbors to come celebrate. "Rejoice with me!" he said. "I have found my lost sheep."

That is the message Jesus wanted His listeners to hear. Like the shepherd, Jesus and the Father rejoice when one of us repents of our sins and comes back to God. In fact, there is more joy among the angels over one sinner who repents than over 99 people who love Jesus and are in church already. Not only that, but Jesus would have come to this earth for just one person!

However, there is more for us to learn about the Shepherd and His sheep. Jesus said, "I am the Good Shepherd. The Good Shepherd lays down His life for the sheep. The hired hand is not the shepherd and does not really care about the sheep. When he sees a wolf coming, he panics and runs away because they are not his sheep. Tragically, the sheep must face the enemy on their own. When the wolf attacks the flock and scatters it, he injures some and kills others.

"Rejoice with me!" he said. "I have found my lost sheep."

"But I am the Good Shepherd," Jesus repeated. "I came to seek and save those who are lost, and I am ready to lay down My life for the sheep." The people in Jesus' day understood the meaning of this parable because they saw shepherds and sheep every day on the hills of Israel.

However, they had no idea that in just a few weeks Jesus would lay down His life for the world. Not only was Jesus the Good Shepherd, but He was also the Lamb of God who took away the sins of the world. He was the Lamb sacrificed on the cross to save you and me. It is a sad story, but we should be glad that Jesus paid the price for us.

Our Prayer:

"Dear Jesus, thank You for coming in search of me when I was lost."

Hidden Treasure Questions:

- ✔ According to this parable, how many people would Jesus have come to this earth to save?
- ✔ Where did the shepherd find his lost sheep?

Listen to this story online!

Scan for bonus content

Good Samaritan

This story is taken from Matthew 22, Mark 12, Luke 10, and *The Desire of Ages*, chapter 54.

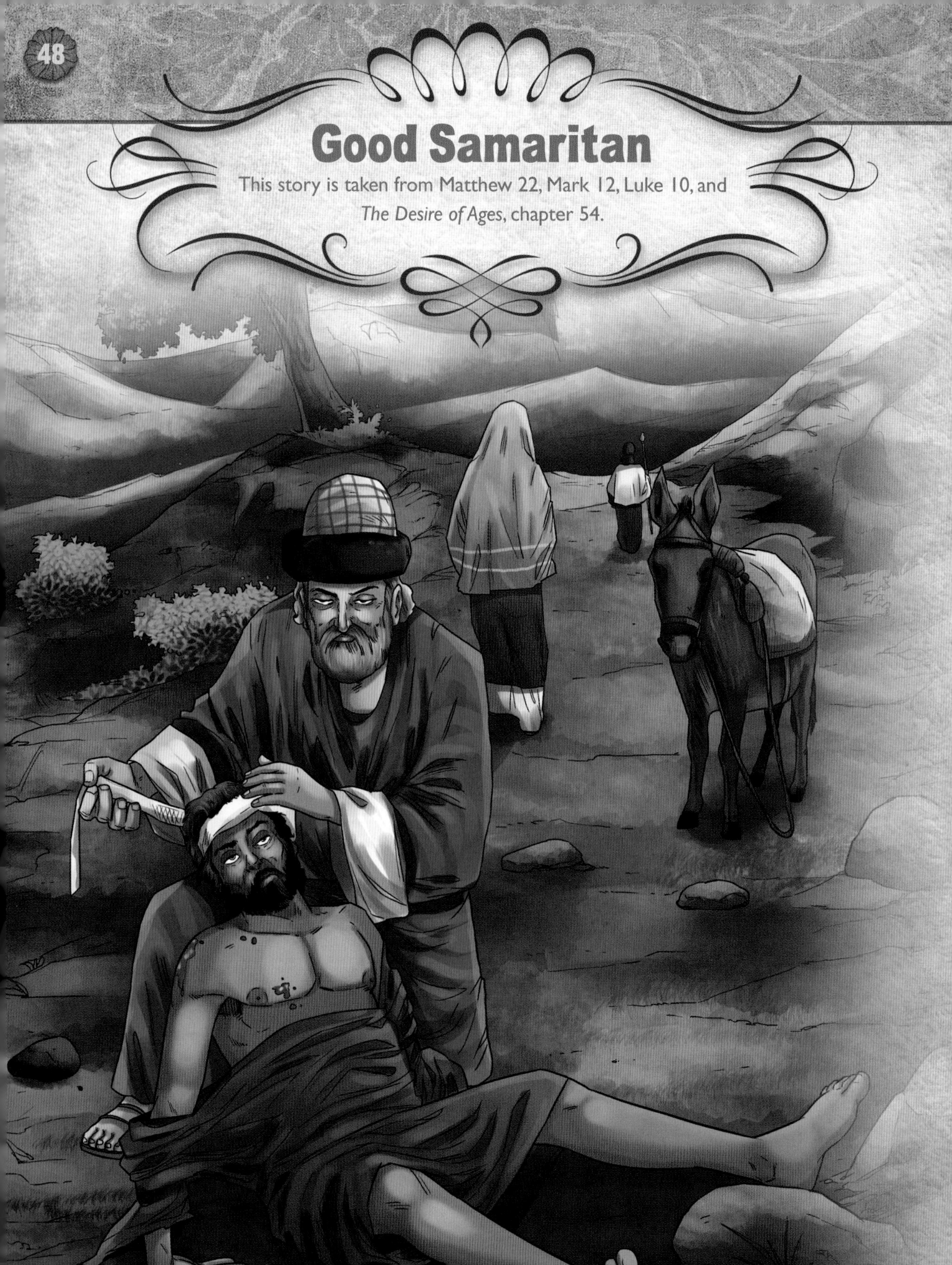

Everybody loves a good story, and in Jesus' day, it was no different. One story Jesus told was about a man who helped others, even though it put himself in great danger. The story was one of Jesus' parables called the Good Samaritan, and today we still like to tell it.

Jesus told the story because of a discussion He had had with a lawyer who wanted to know more about the kingdom of heaven.

"Teacher, what must I do to have eternal life?" the lawyer asked one day when he came to visit Jesus.

"What do the Scriptures say about it?" Jesus said.

The lawyer did not hesitate a second. "That we must love God with all our heart and soul, our strength, and our mind. Besides this, we should love our neighbor as much as we love ourselves."

"That is exactly right!" Jesus replied. "If you do this, you will live forever with God!"

"I have one more question then," the lawyer said. "Who is my neighbor?" The Jews liked some groups of people and hated some. The lawyer wanted Jesus to tell him which ones he absolutely had to love. He had been studying the Scriptures all of his life and was hoping the commandments were not saying that he had to love everyone.

Jesus knew that the lawyer was just looking for a way to avoid having to obey that commandment, so He decided to tell him the story of the Good Samaritan.

When the traveler had gone partway down an empty stretch of the road, bandits attacked him and beat him mercilessly.

A certain man was going on a trip from Jerusalem to Jericho. The road was a long one, stretching 17 miles down through canyons and narrow footpaths. It was a lonely and dangerous old road. Thieves and bandits on that road had attacked many travelers, so it just was not safe.

When the traveler had gone partway down an empty stretch of the road, bandits attacked him. They beat him mercilessly, stripped him of his money and everything he had—even his clothes—and left him to die lying beside the road.

It just so happened that a Jewish priest came along that way. He looked as if he was in a hurry, and who would blame him? That stretch of road was the worst. He saw the poor man lying there and knew he should help him, but he decided not to. Instead, he crossed to the other side of the road and went on his way. It was a terrible thing to pass by the poor man like that! He should have known better, but he did it quickly so he would not have to think about it.

The Samaritan was afraid of the bandits, but he could not ignore the man on the road.

A short time later, another traveler came along that same road. He was a Jewish temple assistant, called a Levite. He was on his way up to Jerusalem to serve in the religious services there. He saw the man all beaten and bloody lying there and went over to get a closer look. He was a worker in the temple and was supposed to help people in need, but he was afraid. If the robbers had beaten and robbed this man, maybe they were waiting nearby for more victims. Therefore, he went on his way, leaving the man to die all alone.

Later that day, a Samaritan came down that road on his donkey and was surprised to see a man all beaten and bruised on the ground. Shadows were probably growing long now in the late-afternoon sun. Like the other travelers before him, the Samaritan was afraid of the bandits, but he could not ignore the man on the road. He was thinking about how he would feel if he was in this poor man's shoes, and he had pity on him.

In Jesus' day, there was a lot of prejudice and hatred between the Samaritans and Jews. A Jew would never talk to a Samaritan, and a Samaritan would not even give a cup of water to a thirsty Jew. That is how much the Jews and Samaritans despised each other.

However, the Samaritan did not care about any of that. Here was a man in need, and he decided that he must help him. He got down off his donkey and knelt beside the man to see what he could do to help him. Carefully he treated the man's wounds with medicine and soothing oil and then bandaged him up to stop the bleeding.

By now, the wounded man must have revived a little, and the Samaritan probably gave him some water to drink. Then he helped the man get on his own donkey and walked beside him to see that he was all right.

When they arrived in Jericho later that evening, the Samaritan took the man to an inn and cared for him all night. The next morning he took out two silver coins and gave them to the innkeeper. "Take care of this man for me," he said. "Let him have a room until he can get back on his feet again. If it costs more than what I have given you, I will pay anything extra when I come back this way again."

Jesus finished His story and looked at the lawyer. "Now, of these three travelers, which would you say was a good neighbor to the man who was robbed?"

"That is easy," the lawyer replied. "The one who showed him some pity, of course."

"Very good," Jesus nodded. "If you would have eternal life, go and do the same."

The parable of the Good Samaritan is a classic, and one that has been told repeatedly since the time of Jesus. It has many good lessons for us and follows the Golden Rule that Jesus quoted from time to time. "Do for others what you would have them do for you."

The next morning the Samaritan took out two silver coins and gave them to the innkeeper.

Who knows? Someday we may need someone to show us kindness. We all know how it feels to need a friend, and how it feels to have that need met. Think about a time when someone shared their lunch with you, helped you do your chores, or prayed with you when you needed it most.

It feels good to be helped, and it feels good to help others. As Jesus said, "It is more blessed to give than to receive." That means we should always think of others before we think of ourselves. Jesus is our example, and like the Good Samaritan, we need to reach out to others so that they will see the love of the Father in us.

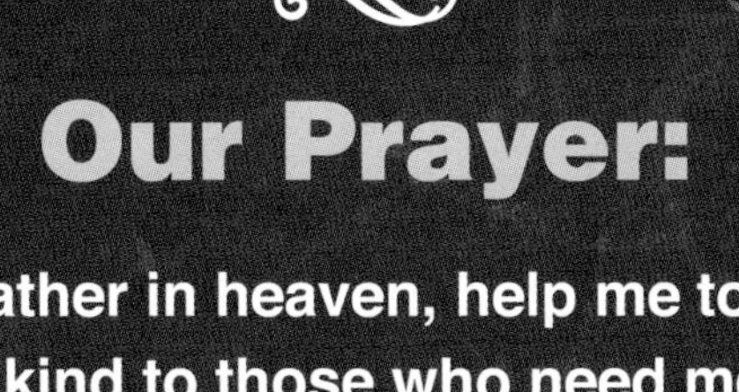

Our Prayer:

"Dear Father in heaven, help me to always be kind to those who need me."

Hidden Treasure Questions:

- ✔ In this story, what question did the lawyer ask Jesus?
- ✔ Who were the three men who came by on the road and saw the victim who had been beaten and robbed by bandits?

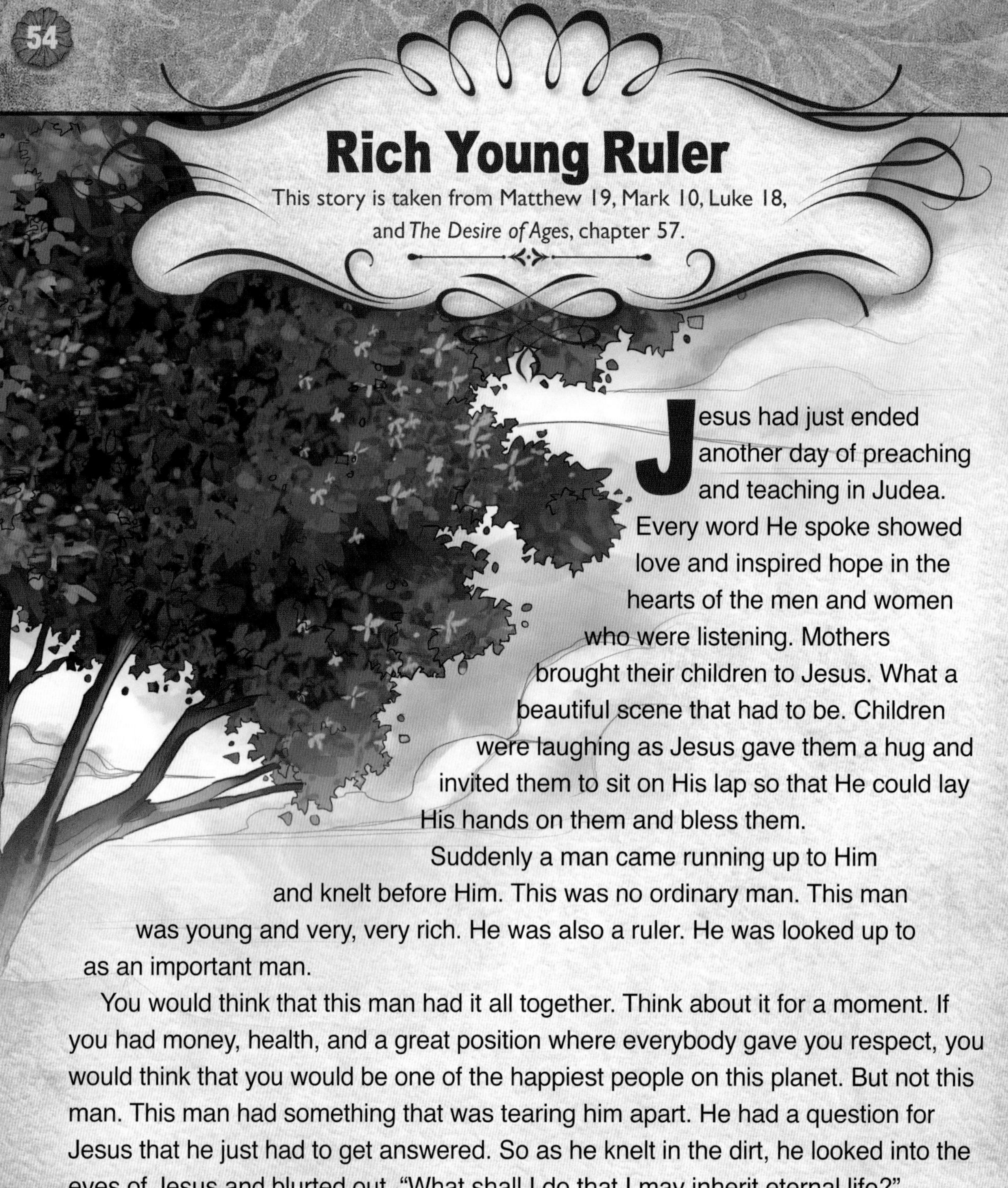

Rich Young Ruler

This story is taken from Matthew 19, Mark 10, Luke 18, and *The Desire of Ages*, chapter 57.

Jesus had just ended another day of preaching and teaching in Judea. Every word He spoke showed love and inspired hope in the hearts of the men and women who were listening. Mothers brought their children to Jesus. What a beautiful scene that had to be. Children were laughing as Jesus gave them a hug and invited them to sit on His lap so that He could lay His hands on them and bless them.

Suddenly a man came running up to Him and knelt before Him. This was no ordinary man. This man was young and very, very rich. He was also a ruler. He was looked up to as an important man.

You would think that this man had it all together. Think about it for a moment. If you had money, health, and a great position where everybody gave you respect, you would think that you would be one of the happiest people on this planet. But not this man. This man had something that was tearing him apart. He had a question for Jesus that he just had to get answered. So as he knelt in the dirt, he looked into the eyes of Jesus and blurted out, "What shall I do that I may inherit eternal life?"

This was a great question, and one that makes Jesus happy when we ask it. This was a heartfelt question. The young man was sincere, and he needed an answer to this question. Jesus looked into this man's eyes and read his heart like a book. He didn't keep him waiting long. He told the young man, "If you want to enter into life, keep the commandments."

"Which ones?" the young man asked.

"You shall not murder. You shall not steal. You shall not bear false witness. Honor your father and mother, and you shall love your neighbor as yourself."

"All these things I have kept from my youth. What do I still lack?" asked the young man.

"If you want to be perfect, go sell all that you have and give it to the poor, and you will have treasure in heaven; and come and follow Me," answered Jesus.

The young man was stunned. He loved God, but there was a problem. He had lots of money, and he was admired by many people every day. Having the admiration of others wasn't the problem, and having money wasn't the problem. The problem was that he loved those things more than he loved God.

Suddenly a man came running up to Jesus and knelt before Him. This man was young and very, very rich.

Those words of Christ must have created a violent tug-of-war in his heart. How could he give up what he treasured the most? Soon the decision was made. He loved what he had too much to give it up. He stood up with a heavy heart, looking like a person who just had the life drained out of him, and walked away sadly.

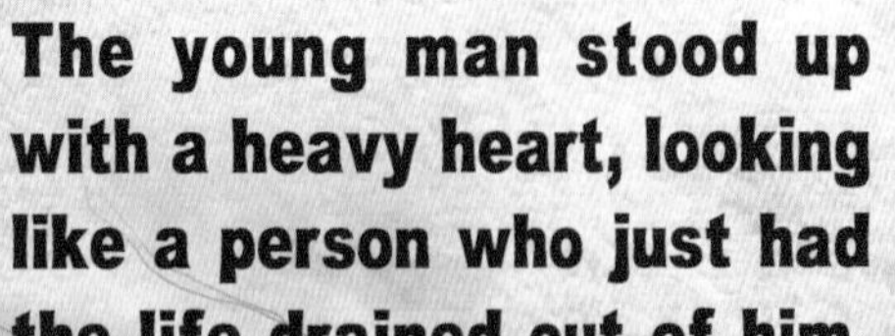

The young man stood up with a heavy heart, looking like a person who just had the life drained out of him, and walked away sadly.

The disciples were shocked with what they had just witnessed. In Bible times, it was commonly thought that if you had wealth and status, it was because God was pleased with you. The problem with a lot of people is that they look only at the outside. If the outside looks good, then they think that the inside must be great, too. Jesus looks at the heart. He knew that this man didn't really have the money. Instead, the money had him.

Jesus could read the minds of the shocked disciples. He knew that He had to answer the questions that they weren't asking. He told them that it is hard for a rich person to make it to the kingdom. He gave them the example of a camel trying to go through the eye of a needle. That would be pretty hard, right? But even that would be easier than a rich man getting into heaven.

When Jesus finished speaking, the disciples asked,

"Who then can be saved?"

"With men this is impossible, but with God all things are possible," He replied.

Christ was saying that God has to be first in our lives. Jesus was trying to teach the disciples something called priority. Priority means to get things in the right order of importance.

Shortly after Jesus started His ministry, He gave His first public lecture on a mountain, which has been called the Sermon on the Mount. During that sermon, Jesus explained that wanting things in life is not bad as long as you do first things first. Jesus said, "Seek first the kingdom of God and His righteousness, and all these things shall be added to you." This is something that the rich young ruler didn't do. He put his riches first and God second.

Let's focus for a minute on what the rich young ruler did right. He believed in God and read His Word. We know that he studied God's Word because he knew the commandments. Then, in his own way, he tried to keep God's commandments. He was obedient up to that point. Obedience is important if we want to be a Christian.

Then the Holy Spirit started working on his conscience, and he did another thing right. He listened. He knew that something in his heart wasn't right, and he went to Jesus to find out what was wrong. So far, so good. We can never go wrong by telling Jesus our problems. So this man did a lot of the right things up to this point.

Then when he had everything going right for him, he did one thing wrong. Jesus recognized all of the good things that he had done. That is why He told the young man that there is "one thing you lack." But the one thing that he lacked was a big thing. Well, we know the rest of the story for this sad man.

But what can we learn from this story for today? Do we have something in our lives that we have to get rid of? It may not be money. It may be that we are not kind to those we play with sometimes. If that is the case, our one thing may be kindness.

Maybe it is jealousy or selfishness. Maybe we have a hard time sharing with others. In that case the one thing that we need is to be less selfish. Remember, Jesus knows what it is like to give up things. He was in heaven and had a wonderful life. He had mansions and golden streets. He could walk, talk, and hold hands with His Father and the angels. He lived in a warm and perfect world without sin.

However, there was one more thing that He wanted. He wanted you and me. He loved heaven, but He wanted to share it with us. That meant He had to give up heaven for a little while and come down here to save us. He came to a world where He wasn't liked by everyone. He came to a world that was cold and cruel. He came to a world that took His very life. Yes, He even gave up His life for you and me.

He did it all because you and I were more important to Him than anything else. The question for you and me today is the same question that the rich young ruler had.

How important is Jesus to you? We have two options. We can follow the rich young ruler's example and walk away sadly with our heads down. Or we can say, "I choose You, Jesus. Help me to give up anything that would keep us apart." Let's make that choice today.

Our Prayer:

"Dear Father, I know that money can sometimes make people selfish. Help me to dedicate everything I have to You, even my money."

Hidden Treasure Questions:

- ✔ Who came to see Jesus and asked what he could do to be saved?
- ✔ Why did Jesus say that it is easier for a camel to go through the eye of a needle than for a rich man to get into heaven?

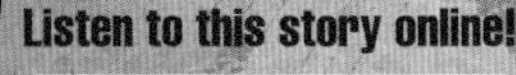

Listen to this story online!

Scan for bonus content

At the Home of Lazarus

This story is taken from Luke 10 and *The Desire of Ages*, chapter 58.

Lazarus was a very close friend of Jesus and one of His most faithful followers. When Jesus came to town, He often stayed at the home of Lazarus in Bethany, a small town not far from Jerusalem. In the home of Lazarus, Jesus could enjoy real rest from the crowds and the troublesome questions that the scribes and Pharisees always brought Him.

Lazarus had two sisters who lived with him in Bethany: Martha and Mary. Martha was the older of the two and was quite a homemaker. She was a good cook and often prepared the meals for special events in Bethany.

Mary was quite different from Martha. When she was young, she had left home and fallen into a sinful life with all the wrong kinds of friends. Then she met Jesus, and He changed her life forever by casting seven demons out of her that had been making her life miserable. Jesus forgave Mary of her sins and told her to leave her sinful life. Not long after that, she returned to her family in Bethany.

One day Jesus and His disciples once again made the long trip up the steep road from Jericho. By the time they arrived in Bethany, they were exhausted. As usual, Martha was a gracious host and invited Jesus to stay with them at their house.

Martha made certain that everything was prepared for Jesus and the disciples whenever they came to visit. Water had to be brought from the city well to bathe their tired, dusty feet. Good food had to be prepared, as well as a place for them to sleep for the night.

And, of course, wherever Jesus went, His disciples went, so that meant Martha needed to have even more food ready. As far as space for sleeping was concerned, it is likely everybody slept on the floor in the inner courtyard.

Martha made certain that everything was prepared for Jesus and the disciples whenever they came to visit.

While the meal was being prepared, Jesus sat with the guests. As usual, He used the opportunity to teach His disciples, and they usually sat around Him in a circle. He knew He did not have much time left on earth, so He took every chance He could to talk with them about the coming kingdom of God.

Mary was there too. She was thirsty for the Water of Life that He was giving, and she sat at His feet to learn as much as she could from Him.

She was so thankful that Jesus had saved her from a sinful life. He had shown her that the heavenly Father loved her, which she would never forget as long as she lived.

Meanwhile, Martha was preparing a tasty meal for everyone and getting ready to serve it. We do not know if Mary even gave her sister a thought, or if she felt she should be helping Martha get things ready.

However, at one point Martha came into the room where Jesus was teaching everyone and told Him that Mary was being lazy. "Lord, don't You care that my sister is not helping me and has left me to serve all by myself? Tell her to come do her part!"

Those are strong words to give the Son of God. The Lord of the universe was in Martha's house offering everyone the Bread of Life, and Martha hardly realized it. She was more worried about how the food would look and taste than receiving some of this heavenly Bread herself.

However, Mary understood what was happening, and Jesus said she had made a good decision.

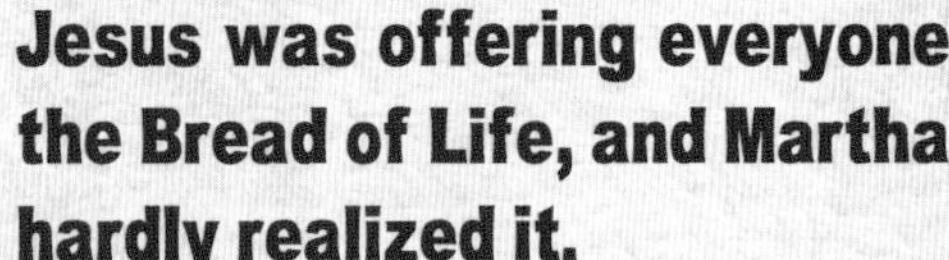

Jesus was offering everyone the Bread of Life, and Martha hardly realized it.

"Martha, Martha, you are worried and troubled about many things," Jesus said. "But one thing is needed, and Mary has chosen that good part, which will not be taken away from her."

We can be sure that He was grateful that Martha was making such a nice meal for Him to eat. But we all know that Jesus was not as interested in eating as He was in saving someone for the kingdom of God.

If Jesus said anything more to Martha, it was probably something like this: "Come, Martha, sit awhile and rest. The food can wait. Let's talk about the things in life that really matter, such as the love My Father in heaven has for you."

There are many things in life that we have to concern ourselves with, but our priority should always be our relationship with Jesus.

Our Prayer:

"Dear Father in heaven, I pray that I will make the choice to sit at Your feet as often as I can."

Hidden Treasure Questions:

- ✔ Which town did Mary, Martha, and Lazarus live in?
- ✔ Why did Mary sit at the feet of Jesus?

Scan for bonus content

A Lesson on True Greatness

This story is taken from Matthew 20, Mark 10, and *The Desire of Ages*, chapter 60.

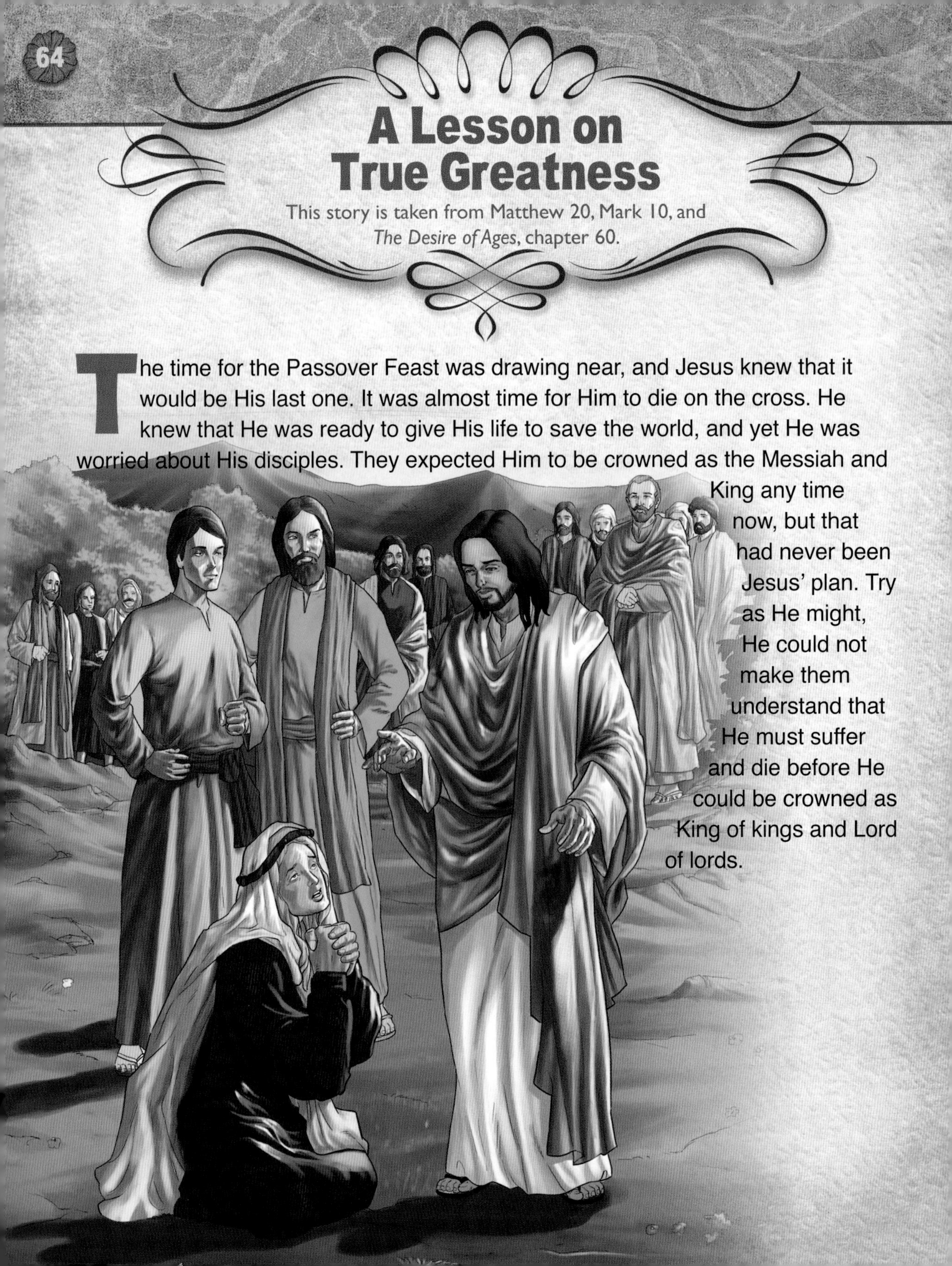

The time for the Passover Feast was drawing near, and Jesus knew that it would be His last one. It was almost time for Him to die on the cross. He knew that He was ready to give His life to save the world, and yet He was worried about His disciples. They expected Him to be crowned as the Messiah and King any time now, but that had never been Jesus' plan. Try as He might, He could not make them understand that He must suffer and die before He could be crowned as King of kings and Lord of lords.

Once again, He called them all together and told them plainly what was coming. "We are going up to Jerusalem," He said. "Someone is going to betray the Son of Man to the chief priests and to the scribes. They will condemn Him to death and deliver Him to the Romans. The soldiers will mock Him, scourge Him, spit on Him, and kill Him. And the third day He will rise again."

The disciples wondered, How could these things be? Jesus had been preaching everywhere that the kingdom of heaven was at hand. He had told the disciples that they would receive positions of high honor in His kingdom. And hadn't the prophets written about the coming glory of the Messiah's reign? So why was Jesus now talking about suffering and death?

One day James and John came with their mother to speak with Jesus. Their mother had a special request.

It made them feel sad to think that Jesus might die, but in their minds, they were sure it would never happen. He had power enough to perform a mighty miracle that would save Him in the end. It was true that the priests and elders at the temple in Jerusalem did not like Him, but His popularity with the common, everyday people in Israel would make up the difference. In the end, they would crown Him King for sure.

Two of Jesus' disciples had especially strong feelings about all of this. John and James had been with Jesus from the start and had grown very close to Him. He had been like a brother to them and a best friend. Every chance they got, they wanted to be close to Him.

They had been anxiously waiting for Jesus to set up His kingdom on earth. Now it seemed that His reign as King was about to begin, in spite of what Jesus was telling them. It was what everybody was expecting.

One day James and John came with their mother to speak with Jesus. Their mother had a special request for her two sons. Kneeling down before Jesus, she humbly asked, "When You become the King of Israel, please allow my sons to sit next to You on Your throne. One on the right side, and the other on Your left."

That was a selfish thing to ask for, especially since Jesus had just been telling His disciples that He was going to suffer and die very soon now. However, that was not the worst of it. The other disciples were furious when they heard what she had requested.

This was not a good thing for Jesus or His disciples. He was having a hard enough time preparing them for what was going to happen when they went to Jerusalem this final time. Now Satan was making it worse.

Jesus knew that He had to take care of this situation. "You do not know what you ask," He said, turning to the two young men. "Are you able to drink the cup that I drink, and be baptized with the baptism that I am baptized with?"

"We can do that," James and John said confidently.

"That's fine," Jesus replied. "You will indeed drink My cup, and be baptized with the baptism that I am baptized with, but to sit on My right hand and on My left is not Mine to give. It's for those for whom it is prepared by My Father."

The other disciples were furious when they heard what she had requested. This was not a good thing for Jesus or His disciples.

Jesus knew that the disciples were angry with James and John. In a way they had a right to be, but He took this chance to teach them all a valuable lesson. "The rulers of this world love to have power so that they can boss other people around," Jesus said, "but for you, it must be different. Whoever wants to become great among you, let him be your servant. Follow My example," Jesus added. "I didn't come to be served, but to serve, and to give My life to save many."

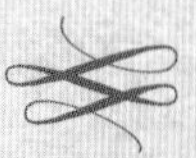

Our Prayer:

"Dear Father in heaven, help me to be as humble as Jesus and willing to serve as a servant."

Hidden Treasure Questions:

- ✔ Who came with James and John to ask for a special favor from Jesus?
- ✔ What was the special favor that James and John's mother asked for?

Scan for bonus content

"Lazarus, Come Forth!"

This story is taken from John 11 and *The Desire of Ages*, chapter 58.

Jesus and Lazarus were best of friends. Since the day Lazarus first met Jesus, his faith in Christ had been strong. There was no doubt in his mind that Jesus was the Messiah and the Savior of the world.

However, right now Lazarus was very sick, and his sisters were worried about him. They tried everything they could think of to help him get well, but nothing was working. Medicines were not helping, and neither were herbs. Even the doctors could do nothing to help him. Martha and Mary were desperate! "If Jesus were here, He would know what to do," they kept telling each other. Jesus had stayed in their home many times. They loved Jesus as a brother and treated Him as family. Unfortunately, He was nowhere around.

Finally, when it seemed that all hope was gone, the two sisters sent someone to find Jesus. "Please come, Lord," the messengers said. "Your good friend Lazarus is sick."

When Jesus received the message, He said, "This sickness is not unto death, but for the glory of God that the Son of God may be glorified through it." Jesus wanted them to know that He was the Messiah and the Son of God. He did not go to Bethany to see Lazarus right away. It was painful to wait and make the family suffer, but Jesus knew that it was for the best in the end. Jesus was saving His best and most famous miracle for His friend Lazarus. Because He waited, many would now see the power of God and come to accept Him as their Savior.

Lazarus was very sick, and his sisters were worried about him. They tried everything they could think of to help him get well.

For those who were trusting Jesus to do what was best, the promise was waiting to be fulfilled. All things work together for the good of those who love God.

Jesus stayed where He was for two more days. Then He said, "Let us go to Judea again."

The disciples were surprised when Jesus said they were going to Bethany of Judea. They wanted to help Lazarus, but they thought it was too dangerous. "Rabbi, are You really thinking of going there again?" they said to Him. "Lately the Jews in Judea want to stone You."

Jesus ignored the warnings from His disciples because He knew that God had a special job for Him to do in Bethany. "Our friend Lazarus

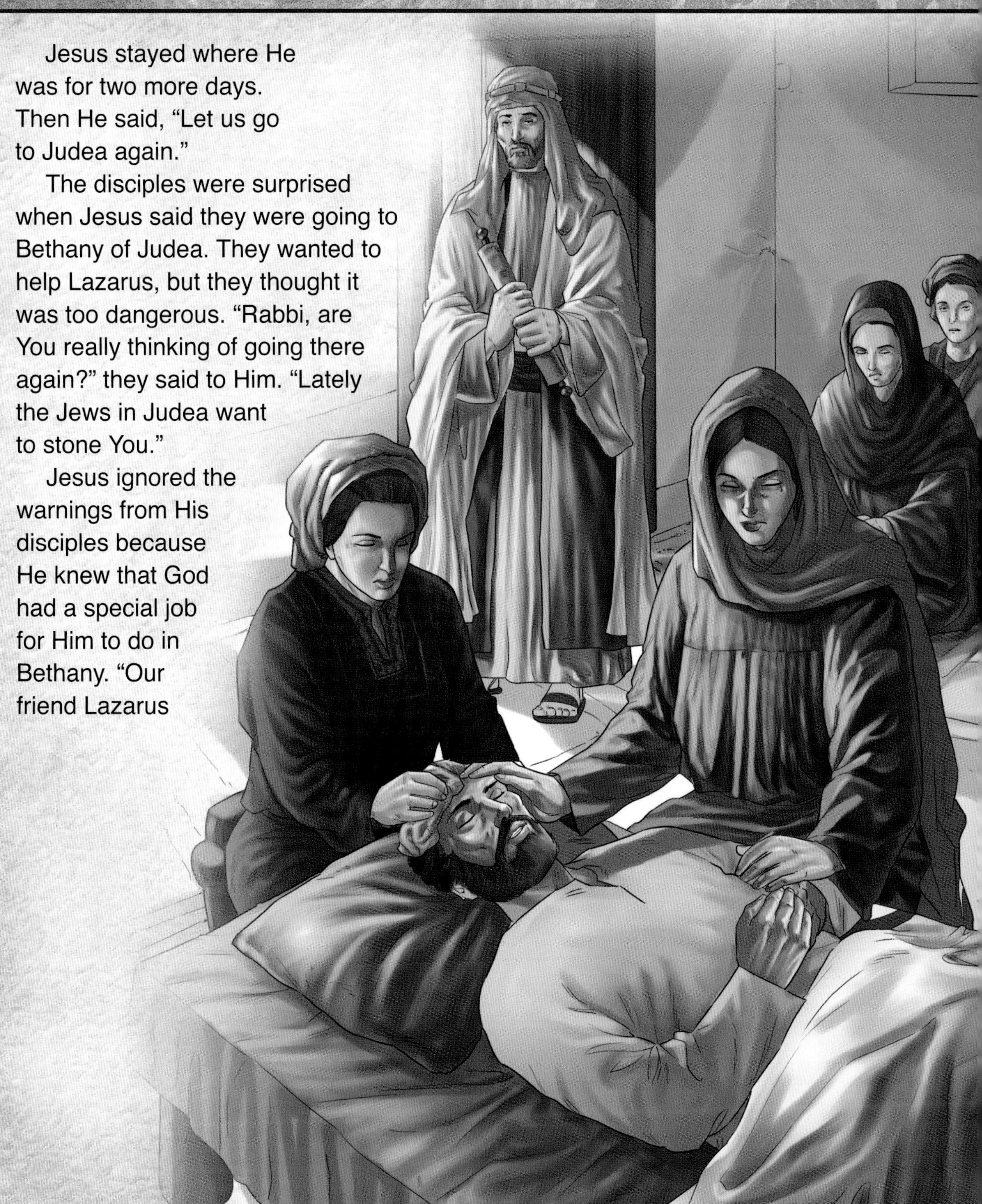

sleeps," Jesus said. "But I go that I may wake him up."

"Lord, if he sleeps, he will get well," the disciples said.

But Jesus shook His head and said plainly, "Lazarus is dead."

The disciples must have been shocked at this news because Lazarus was a good friend of them all. They enjoyed staying at his house every time they went to Bethany, and they all enjoyed eating Martha's cooking.

When they arrived at the tomb, Jesus told them to take away the stone from the entrance.

"It is best for everyone this way," Jesus added. "I was not there, and that was God's plan so that many of you may believe in what I have been doing. Now it is time. Let us all go see him."

Some of the disciples still tried talking Jesus out of going to Judea, because they knew He would be in enemy territory. However, Thomas finally said, "We cannot let Jesus go alone. Let's all go to Jerusalem, so that we can die with Him."

So they made the trip to Judea. When they arrived, they learned that Lazarus had been dead and in the tomb for four days already. By now, many people had come to join Martha and Mary to mourn the loss of Lazarus.

When news reached Martha that Jesus had

arrived, she went out to meet Him. "Lord, if You had been here, my brother would not have died," she said. "However, I know that whatever You ask of God, He will give You."

Jesus did not seem the least bit worried and tried to comfort her. "Your brother will rise again," He said.

"Yes, I know he will rise again on the resurrection morning," Martha replied.

"I am the resurrection and the life," Jesus said confidently. "He who believes in Me, though he may die, he shall live. Do you believe this?"

"Yes, Lord," Martha said, "I believe that You are the Christ, the Son of God, who is to come into this world."

Then Martha went to Mary and whispered that Jesus had come and was asking for her. Immediately Mary went out to find Jesus, and all the relatives and mourners followed her, thinking that she might be going to the tomb of Lazarus.

When Mary reached Jesus, she fell down at His feet and cried as though her heart would break. Like her sister, she could not understand why Jesus had waited. If Jesus had come in time, she knew Lazarus would not have died.

"Where is he buried?" Jesus kindly asked.

"Come and see," they said.

Jesus wept. He was moved by their sorrow. He began to cry with the family too, but it was not because Lazarus was dead, for He knew that He was about to call him from the grave.

Jesus was crying because people were making terrible decisions that would cost them eternal life. For example, He knew that many of those who were mourning for Lazarus would soon be planning His death on the cross. He also saw that the nation of Israel would reject Him as their Savior, and this would eventually bring the destruction of Jerusalem by the Romans.

When they arrived at the tomb, Jesus told them to take away the stone from the entrance.

"Lord, by this time there is an odor of death in the tomb!" Martha said in surprise. "Our brother has been dead for four days!"

Jesus ignored her warning. "Didn't I say that if you believe, the name of God would be honored and praised?"

Then they took away the stone from the place where Lazarus was lying. A hush must have fallen over the crowd by now. They must have all wondered, "What will Jesus do?" But they did not have long to wait.

"Lazarus, come forth!" To everyone's shock, that is exactly what happened!

Jesus looked toward heaven and prayed, "Father, I want to thank You that You always hear Me." Then He called, "Lazarus, come forth!"

To everyone's shock, that is exactly what happened! Lazarus came out of the tomb still bound up in the graveclothes.

"Loose him, and let him go!" Jesus said.

The resurrection of Lazarus from the dead was Jesus' greatest miracle. Because of this miracle, Jesus became even more famous, and many now wanted to crown Him as the Messiah.

However, the Jewish leaders who witnessed the miracle were jealous and left the tomb determined more than ever to find a way to kill Jesus.

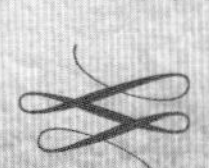

Our Prayer:

"Dear Jesus, I am so glad that You have power over death and the grave."

Hidden Treasure Questions:

- ✔ What were the names of the two sisters of Lazarus?
- ✔ When Jesus finally came to the tomb of Lazarus, how many days had he been dead?

Church Leaders Plan a Murder

This story is taken from John 11 and *The Desire of Ages*, chapter 59.

Many who witnessed the resurrection of Lazarus were impressed with the power of God and came to believe in Jesus as the Messiah. This miracle was now the latest and the greatest proof from heaven that Jesus was indeed the Son of God. It had been done in broad daylight near the city of Jerusalem, and could not be denied. There were too many witnesses.

Some who were at the tomb that day were spies, and they took reports of the amazing miracle back to Jerusalem. When the chief priests and Pharisees heard what had happened, they called a special meeting of the Sanhedrin.

These men knew what the prophecies said about the Messiah. They remembered seeing Jesus as a boy in Jerusalem, telling the temple teachers that the Messiah must come to die for the sins of the world. They remembered how inspired they felt that He was a very unusual boy, and that He might even be the Messiah Himself.

Now they could see that Jesus was fulfilling all the signs that pointed to Him as the Son of God. He could be the Messiah, and yet they refused to admit it. As the religious leaders of Israel, they were more interested in the political power that they held over the common people, and less about Jesus being their Savior from sin.

There were a few religious leaders who supported Jesus, such as Nicodemus, Joseph of Arimathea, and Simon the Pharisee. However, most of the Pharisees and Sadducees had rejected Jesus as the Messiah long ago. It was plain to see that if they did not do something to stop Jesus soon, their future as leaders in Israel was nearing an end.

"What are we going to do?" they fearfully asked one another. "We have a real problem now."

"We are just going to have to find a way to get rid of Him," others said angrily. "But how? Things

Some who were at the tomb that day were spies, and they took reports.

are really getting out of hand. We should have done something a long time ago!"

Caiaphas was the high priest that year, and he saw what was happening to divide the group of religious leaders. He was a proud, cruel man, and only pretended to be godly so that he could get power and wealth for himself. He had studied the prophecies about the Messiah, and though he did not understand them accurately, he finally spoke up with authority.

"Calm down, everyone!" we can hear him say as he took over the discussion. "You people are all getting upset over nothing! The prophecies have foretold that this very thing will happen. It may be that one Man will have to die for the people so that the whole nation does not perish. Maybe this Jesus of Nazareth is the One who must die!"

Even if Jesus was innocent, Caiaphas said that they must get rid of Him, and the other leaders began to listen to his advice. Jesus was trouble for the nation because He divided everyone, causing the people to question the temple leaders.

"If we let this Jesus of Nazareth go on performing miracles, soon everyone will believe in Him and will set Him up as the Messiah. Then there will be a revolt against the Romans, and the Roman army will come and destroy our temple and the nation. Is that what God wants?" Caiaphas demanded. "It is clear that this will not be a good thing for Israel. We can be sure that God does not want our nation to be destroyed," he said with fire in his eyes. "So I think we all know what needs to be done."

This was not a new idea at all. It was one that pagan nations surrounding Israel often taught. To satisfy the gods when they were angry, people thought they needed to offer a human sacrifice. In that case, one person would die for the nation.

The leaders began making plans immediately about how they could kill Jesus.

Caiaphas knew that the sins of the world would one day have to be paid for by the Lamb of God and that the Scriptures foretold this. However, he did not fully realize that Jesus was the Son of God and the Lamb who would take away the sins of the world. Even worse, Caiaphas did not fully understand that he and the other leaders of the Sanhedrin were going to be the ones to fulfill that prophecy.

The leaders began making plans immediately about how they could kill Jesus. Jesus knew this, of course, but He also knew that He could not give Himself up to them until the coming Passover Feast, which was only a few days away.

Therefore, Jesus left Judea and went out to stay in the woods, where He could spend the few remaining days with His disciples.

Our Prayer:

"Dear Jesus, help me not to reject the wonderful truths You have for me in the Bible, as the Pharisees and Sadducees did."

Hidden Treasure Questions:

- ✔ What was the name of the high priest in Jerusalem?
- ✔ Why would they want to kill Jesus?

Listen to this story online!

Scan for bonus content

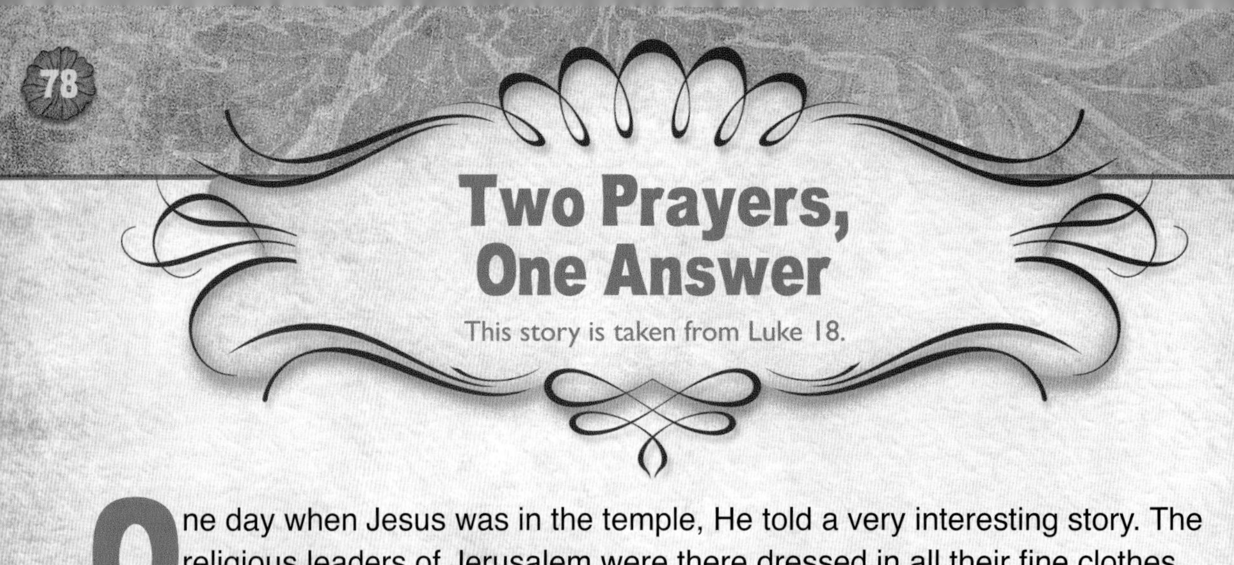

Two Prayers, One Answer

This story is taken from Luke 18.

One day when Jesus was in the temple, He told a very interesting story. The religious leaders of Jerusalem were there dressed in all their fine clothes, but many common, everyday people were there, too.

Jesus knew that most of the priests and Pharisees thought very highly of themselves. Instead of depending on God for their salvation, they depended on their own works. They also believed that God loved them more than any other group of people. In a way that they would understand, Jesus knew that He had to tell the people that this wasn't true. That is why He told this story.

Two men went to the temple one morning to pray. One was a Pharisee and the other a publican or tax collector.

The city of Jerusalem was already busy with traffic as the two men passed through the streets on their way to the temple. Young girls with water jars on their heads were coming from the city well. In the marketplace, women bought figs, grapes, and pomegranates at the little shops lining the streets. Old men sat together near the temple gate, warming themselves in the morning sunshine.

Two men went to the temple one morning to pray. One was a Pharisee and the other a publican.

The crowds of worshippers hadn't arrived yet when the Pharisee and publican entered through the temple gate. However, the temple merchants were already bringing in their calves, lambs, and goats to sell for sacrifices. Those who sold doves were bringing in their cages of birds. A money changer sat against the courtyard wall, busily counting out stacks of coins and putting them on a low table in front of him. There were copper coins, and silver ones, and some even of gold.

Now, the Pharisee was a proud man, full of self-righteousness. He was the kind of man who bragged all day long about his good deeds. As usual, he made sure that everyone saw how he was dressed as he passed through the crowds. Long sleeves and tassels decorated the Pharisee's fine temple robe. He also wore little leather boxes with Bible verses in them called phylacteries, which he tied to his wrists and forehead. He did this so that everyone would know that he was keeping all of God's Ten Commandments.

The publican was not a poor man either, but he had a bad reputation. His robe was made of brightly colored cloth. It was the kind worn by the rich and famous who liked to go to social parties. By the way he was dressed, everyone could tell that he was a tax collector hired by the hated Roman government. It was well-known that tax collectors were thieves, because they always asked for too much money when they taxed the people. Everyone watching knew that the publican was not a nice man, and not someone they would ever want to have as a friend.

The Pharisee went to stand by himself away from the other worshippers so that everyone would notice him.

The Pharisee walked across the wide temple courtyard and into the temple. As he passed the rich people, the priests, and the scribes on his way, he swished his robe and smiled a good morning. However, when he passed the common people, he kept his nose high in the air.

The publican followed the Pharisee, but was careful to stay behind him. He walked with shuffling feet and his head down. As he passed people, he did not say good morning. He knew that he had done many bad things in his life, but he wanted to come to the temple to pray. He knew that he needed God more than anything.

As always, the Pharisee had come to show off his

money and to remind everyone that he was much better than any of them. As he stopped at the offering box, he slowly pulled a bag of copper coins from the pockets of his long robe. After looking around to see if everyone was watching, he slowly dumped the clattering coins into the offering box. Copper coins made just as much noise as gold and silver ones, but they didn't cost as much.

The publican had money to give, but he knew that it would not be accepted. No one would exchange his money for temple shekels, which was the money needed for offerings. "Your money's no good here!" a money exchanger growled at the publican. Any money the publican might give was considered evil, because it had been earned by collecting taxes for the Romans. And they knew that the publican had gotten rich doing just that.

The Pharisee went to stand by himself away from the other worshippers so that everyone would notice him. He stood tall and straight, raised his face to the ceiling far above, and prayed. "God, I thank You that I am not like other men. I am not a thief nor a murderer. I don't cheat or tell lies, and I give money for the poor now and then. I am not at all like this tax collector," he said as he pointed toward the publican. "I fast twice a week; I give tithes of all that I possess."

The people standing nearby bowed their heads with respect to the Pharisee as they watched him pray. "The Pharisee is rich; therefore, he must be a very holy man," they said among themselves.

The publican stood off to one side and would not even raise his eyes to heaven, but struck his chest with his hand again and again. "Please, God, be merciful to me, for I am a sinner!" he cried out.

The crowd could see that the publican and Pharisee were very different from one another, standing there in the temple court. The Pharisee was proud and conceited, but the publican had tears running down his face.

Jesus looked at the people who were listening to His story. "Now, which one of these two men do you think was closer to God that day?" He asked. "I tell you, it was the publican. The Pharisee did not even really think he needed God, but the publican had humbled himself before God, and so the peace of heaven was in his heart."

We should not be proud of our possessions, and we should not be bragging about what we do.

Jesus said, "'It is more blessed to give than to receive.'" Both the Pharisee and the publican needed to think about that. They both enjoyed receiving more than giving, but the publican wanted that to change. The Pharisee did not.

That is what it is like today in our churches. We should not be proud of our possessions, and we should not be bragging about what we do. God is not as interested in how much we give Him as He is in how we give it. If we listen to His voice, He will tell us how much we should give and when. Both the publican and the Pharisee needed to learn that lesson.

Our Prayer:

"Dear Father in heaven, I pray that I will be more like the publican when I come to church to worship, and less like the Pharisee."

Hidden Treasure Questions:

- ✔ If you could be one or the other, who would you be, the publican or the Pharisee?
- ✔ Why do you think people treated the Pharisee so nicely, but were not kind to the publican? Do you think it was right for them to do that?

Listen to this story online!

Scan for bonus content

Zacchaeus

This story is taken from Luke 19 and *The Desire of Ages*, chapter 61.

Jesus traveled through the city of Jericho from time to time with His disciples on His trips from Galilee and the towns across the Jordan. The city of Jericho had a warm climate, with palm trees and gardens fed by many springs of water. It was a tourist town and drew all kinds of people for parties, gambling, and entertainment. King Herod himself had a winter palace there, to which he came on holidays.

Jericho was a town of business, too. For thousands of years, it had been the crossroads for trade in the Jordan Valley. Caravans of camels and donkeys passed through Jericho on their way north or south, bringing the riches of foreign countries with them.

The collection of taxes there made Jericho the home of many publicans, and Zacchaeus was the most famous one of them all. He was a Jew, but he might as well have been a Gentile, because he worked for the Romans collecting taxes. As chief tax collector, he was considered the enemy of all Jews, and almost everybody hated him.

Zacchaeus spotted a sycamore tree down the street. He ran ahead to climb the tree so that he could get a good look at Jesus.

In the days of Jesus, tax collectors were cheaters and thieves. They would tax you for anything and everything they could possibly get out of you. If you had to sell your home to pay a tax debt, your loss was their gain.

Because of the way Zacchaeus made a living, no one would invite him to their homes, and he was not allowed in the synagogue. It was a lonely life for a man like Zacchaeus, and though he was very wealthy, he had few friends in Jericho. The only kind of people who would come to his house for dinner or a party were other tax collectors and other people whom no one else liked.

Zacchaeus was a proud man, but the Holy Spirit was calling him to a better way of life. He had heard about the miracles that Jesus had performed to help the sick. He had heard that Jesus accepted outcasts such as tax collectors and lepers, whom everyone else rejected.

He had always wanted to see Jesus, but every time that Jesus came through Jericho, somehow he always missed Him. Because Zacchaeus was a tax collector, no one would make way for him in the crowds.

One day he heard that Jesus was coming through Jericho again, and he was very excited. As he saw the crowds coming down the street, he tried his best to catch a glimpse of Jesus, but he was a very short man. He could not see over the heads of the people who were pressing around Jesus in the crowds that followed Him.

Then Zacchaeus spotted a sycamore tree down the street. He ran ahead of the crowd to climb the tree so that he could get a good look at Him.

As Jesus was passing under the tree, He looked up and saw the tax collector sitting on a branch. The crowd surrounding Him was surprised to see the rich man sitting in a tree, but Jesus just smiled.

"Come down, Zacchaeus," He said. "Today I must stay at your house."

So Zacchaeus quickly climbed down out of the tree and took Jesus and His disciples to his house. He was so happy! He could not believe that Jesus would visit with him in his home! No Jewish rabbi or Pharisee would ever do that!

Zacchaeus quickly climbed down out of the tree and took Jesus and His disciples to his house.

When people in the crowd saw Jesus going away to eat dinner with Zacchaeus, they complained, "He's going to be a guest in the home of a man who is a sinner."

But the disciples probably were not surprised to see Jesus go to the home of a tax collector. After all, Matthew, one of Jesus' closest disciples, had been a tax collector.

Zacchaeus welcomed Jesus into his house, and we can imagine it was a meal to remember. He felt so honored to have the Lord in his home! Jesus had accepted him and forgiven him for the life of sin that he had lived. Standing to his feet at the end of the meal, Zacchaeus made a very important announcement.

"Lord, I want to make things right," he said. "Starting this day, I am going to give half of all that I own to the poor. And if I have taken anything from anyone unfairly, I will give back four times as much."

Jesus was very pleased to see such a change in Zacchaeus. He said, "Today salvation has come to the home of this man who is a son of Abraham." We too can have salvation in Jesus. All we have to do is accept Him.

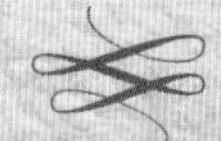

Our Prayer:

"Dear Jesus, help me to be willing to accept everyone and love them as You did."

Hidden Treasure Questions:

- ✔ What was the name of the short man who wanted to see Jesus?
- ✔ What did this short man do for a living?

The Best Gift Jesus Ever Received

This story is taken from Matthew 26, Mark 14, Luke 7, John 12, and *The Desire of Ages*, chapter 62.

Jesus was always being invited to eat at someone's house. Rich people knew it was a popular thing to have Him in their home. Religious leaders wanted to find out who He was. Then there were those who were grateful for what He had done for them. Simon the Pharisee was just such a person.

Simon had been a very important man in Israel, but before he met Jesus, he was not a very nice person. As a Pharisee, he would walk down the street with his fancy clothes on, praying loud prayers so that others could see and hear him. He would send trumpeters ahead of him in the street or synagogue to announce that he was about ready to give money to the poor. He was one of those who would show off his tithes and offerings by bringing bags of coins that would rattle and clatter in the metal offering boxes in the temple.

Mary began to cry. She wiped Jesus' feet with her long, flowing hair.

Everyone had always thought Simon was a wonderful person who had a place in heaven already saved for him. But there was another side of Simon that no one knew. Sometimes he did things that he knew were wrong, and later he would be ashamed of them.

Then Simon became a leper. This was the worst thing that could happen to a Pharisee, because he could no longer be a religious leader for his people. Even worse, he would have to leave home and live away from family and friends in a leper colony somewhere.

"How could a man of God get leprosy?" everyone wondered. They had been taught that only sinners got such diseases as leprosy. Of course, we know that Simon was a sinner who had done many bad things, but at that time nobody knew about his secret life.

Then Simon met Jesus, and his life was changed forever. Jesus knew all about Simon's secret life, but He healed him of his terrible disease anyway. Even more important, He forgave all of Simon's sins.

Although he thought Jesus was an excellent teacher and hoped He might be the Messiah, Simon was not ready to accept Him as the Savior of the world.

To show his appreciation for what Jesus had done for him, Simon invited Him to his home for a banquet.

Other important people were there too, including Jesus' disciples. Lazarus, whom Jesus had raised from the dead, was also there, along with his sisters, Martha and Mary.

As usual, Martha was serving the food, but Mary sat close to Jesus to listen to His words of life. Jesus had cast the demons out of her and forgiven her sins. Now she wanted to follow Him and be one of His disciples, too.

Judas began complaining to the other disciples.

When people went to banquets in those days, they did not sit on chairs as people do in many countries today. They did not sit on the floor, either. Instead, they sat or lay on couches that surrounded low serving tables on which all the food was set. In this way, everyone's face was close to the food, and their feet pointed away from the table.

It was at this feast that Mary decided to give Jesus a very special gift. She had heard Jesus say that He was going to die shortly, and although none of the other disciples really believed Him, she did. She had been saving her money for a long time to buy an alabaster jar of very expensive perfume. The perfume, called spikenard, was from rose petals, and for a person without much money, it could cost a whole year's wages. Spikenard was used on rare occasions such as weddings and funerals, which is why Mary bought it. She felt it would be better to put the perfume on Jesus while He was alive than when He was dead.

She wanted to pour the perfume on Jesus at the banquet to show Him how much she loved Him for saving her from a life of sin. However, she tried to anoint Him without everyone noticing.

The alabaster jars used in those days for spikenard perfume had no lid on them, so when they were broken open, they had to be used all at one time. Mary must not have thought about how strong the fragrance would be, because when she broke the jar open and poured the perfume on Jesus' head and feet, the fragrance filled the room. She began to cry. Her love for Jesus was part of why she was crying, but she may also have been embarrassed because the fragrance was so overpowering, and everyone was looking at her. She wiped Jesus' feet with her long, flowing hair. Now everyone in the room could smell the spikenard and knew what she had done.

Instead of people smiling at the expensive gift she was giving to Jesus, some began to frown. Judas began complaining to the other disciples that the perfume could have been sold and the money given to the poor.

Jesus knew what they were all thinking. "Why are you criticizing her?" He asked. "She has done a good thing for Me. You will always have the poor with you, but you will not always have Me. She has poured this perfume on Me to prepare My body for burial. She will always be remembered for this deed. The story of what she has done will be told throughout the whole world, wherever the good news of the gospel is preached."

When Simon saw Mary putting the perfume on Jesus' feet, he thought to himself that Jesus must not be the Messiah. If He were, He would have known that Mary was a sinner and would not have let her touch Him.

That is not how Jesus treated people. Furthermore, He knew what Simon was thinking and decided to teach him a lesson on love and forgiveness.

"Though Mary has many sins, she is forgiven much, because she loved much."

"There were two men who owed money to a banker," Jesus said to Simon. "One of the men owed the banker 500 denarii, and the other 50. Now, neither of the two men could pay the debt, and yet the banker freely forgave them both. Tell Me, Simon, which of these two men would love the banker more?"

Simon said, "I suppose the one who was forgiven more."

"Exactly," Jesus replied. "Now take this woman, for example," and He turned to look at Mary, who was still drying His feet with her hair. "You never washed My feet with water when I came into your house. You never gave Me a welcoming kiss.

"However, this woman has anointed Me with perfume, has washed My feet with her tears and wiped them with her hair, and has not stopped kissing My feet since I arrived. Therefore, though she has many sins, she is forgiven much, because she loved much."

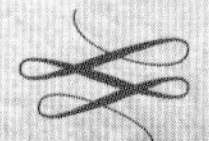

Our Prayer:

"Dear Jesus, help me not to criticize others, but love them like You did."

Hidden Treasure Questions:

- What was the name of the Pharisee who invited Jesus to a banquet?
- Who complained because Mary spent so much on the perfume?

Scan for bonus content

The Unforgiving Servant

This story is taken from Matthew 18.

Jesus was always looking for opportunities to teach His disciples lessons that would be helpful to them in their ministry. Showing mercy was one character trait that He wanted His followers to have, and so was forgiveness. If they could develop these traits, they would become more like the Father in heaven.

One day Peter came to Jesus to ask Him a question. "Lord, how often should I forgive my brother who has sinned against me? Up to seven times?"

We do not know exactly what it was that made him ask the question. However, it was likely that someone had done something to him, and he was probably finding it difficult to be forgiving. However, after having walked and talked with Jesus for more than two years, he probably wanted to be more like Him.

Most Jews considered three times to be a great number when it came to acts of kindness or forgiveness. Peter thought that he was going the extra mile when he suggested forgiving his brother seven times.

Forgiving a brother was one thing. Forgiving a stranger or a foreigner such as a Samaritan was another thing altogether. No Jew thought it was important or necessary to forgive a Samaritan, even once.

So Jesus' answer to Peter must have been a real shock. "Forgiving your brother seven times isn't enough," Jesus said. "Actually, 70 times seven would be better for your brother, or anyone, for that matter."

The idea that Jesus was trying to teach His disciples was that forgiveness cannot be measured or counted. If it is, it isn't really forgiveness. If we want to forgive, then it won't make any difference whether we are asked to forgive seven times, or 70 times seven, or 700 times seven.

Peter should not have been surprised that Jesus would say such a thing. Hadn't he already heard Jesus say things such as "Love your enemies. Say nice things to those who curse you. Do good to those who hate you. And pray for those who are mean to you"?

Jesus then told His disciples a parable to show them what forgiveness should be all about.

The servant fell on his face in front of the king. "Master," he begged, "have patience with me, and I will pay you everything I owe!"

The kingdom of heaven can be described like this: There once was a king who wanted to settle accounts with his servants. When he began to settle these accounts, one servant was brought to him who owed 10,000 talents. That amount of money could not have been repaid in 100 lifetimes. The point is, it was impossible to pay that money back. So the king ordered him to be sold, with his wife and children and all that he had. That way, at least a little payment could be made for his debt.

The servant was frightened at the thought of himself and his family being sold as slaves. He fell on his face in front of the king. "Master," he begged, "have patience with me, and I will pay you everything I owe!" The king knew this was impossible.

However, the king felt sorry for his servant and released him. But he did more than that—he forgave him the debt.

As the servant went out on the street, he chanced to meet one of his fellow servants who owed him 100 denarii. This debt was nothing compared to the debt for which he had just been shown mercy and forgiveness. To everyone's surprise, the servant grabbed the man by the throat and shouted, "Pay me what you owe!"

The fellow servant fell down at his feet. "Give me time, and I will pay the debt!" he begged.

The servant who had owed 10,000 talents would not forgive him. In fact, he took the man and put him in prison.

But the servant who had owed 10,000 talents would not forgive him. In fact, he took the man and put him in prison till he could pay the debt of 100 denarii.

When his fellow servants saw this, they were very upset and went to tell the king everything that had happened.

The king called for the first servant and said to him, "You wicked servant! I forgave you all that money you owed me because you begged me. Shouldn't you also have had compassion on your fellow servant, just as I had pity on you?"

The king was very angry and sent that ungrateful servant to prison until he should pay all that was due him.

So it is with the heavenly Father. Those who have been forgiven much by Him should be willing to forgive much. Those who are not willing to forgive cannot expect any mercy.

God's grace covers all our sins. Let us show how grateful we are for His gift of forgiveness by forgiving others.

Our Prayer:

"Dear Jesus, help me to be like You and forgive others when they don't treat me nicely."

Hidden Treasure Questions:

- ✔ How many times did Jesus tell Peter that he should be willing to forgive his brother?
- ✔ Which of the two servants had a debt that was impossible to repay?

Scan for bonus content

Jesus' Triumphal Entry

This story is taken from Matthew 21, Mark 11, Luke 19, John 12, and *The Desire of Ages*, chapter 63.

It was less than a week now before Jesus would die. However, before He should lay down His life for the world, He needed to do something very special. This happened one day while He and His disciples were on their way to Jerusalem.

As they were passing by the little village of Bethphage on the Mount of Olives, Jesus told two of His disciples, "Go into the village, and there inside the city gate you will find a donkey tied and its baby colt with it. Let them loose and bring them to Me. If the owner asks what you are doing, tell him 'The Lord needs them.' When you tell him that, he will send the donkey with you willingly."

Jesus told two of His disciples, "Go into the village, and there inside the city gate you will find a donkey tied and its baby colt."

Jesus knew that it was time to fulfill the prophecy in Scripture that pointed to Him as the Messiah. This famous verse written in the book of Zechariah said, "Tell the daughter of Zion, 'Behold, your King is coming to you, lowly, and sitting on a donkey, a colt, the foal of a donkey.'"

So the disciples did as Jesus asked. They found the donkey with a colt tied up inside the village gate, exactly as He had told them they would.

Before long they were back, and then Jesus told everybody the surprise. It was time for Him to ride into Jerusalem on the donkey as King. When Jesus told them this, the disciples got excited! Did this mean that Jesus was actually going to publicly announce that He was the Messiah? Riding on the donkey was exactly what a Messiah King would do.

Quickly, the disciples laid their coats and cloaks on the donkey's back. Then they set Jesus on the donkey, and Lazarus, who was with them, began leading it up the road to Jerusalem. As they walked along, the disciples broke off palm branches and began waving them. "Hosanna to the Son of David!" they shouted. "Blessed is He who comes in the name of the Lord."

As they walked up over the Mount of Olives, people began joining them. Soon a whole crowd was following Jesus. Some people spread their coats on the road for the donkey to walk on, while others cut down palm branches and spread them on the road too. That was what people did in those days when a king came riding through town.

But this was no ordinary man, and He would be no ordinary king! This was a Man who could heal the blind. He could walk on water and cleanse the lepers. He could multiply loaves and fish. He could even raise the dead! This Man did miracles like no one who had ever lived in Israel. And it should be no surprise. After all, He was the Son of God!

Everyone was getting very excited. It looked as if Jesus was finally going to allow them to crown Him King. "Hosanna to the Son of David!" the crowds shouted together. "Blessed is He who comes in the name of the Lord! Hosanna in the highest!"

As they walked up over the Mount of Olives, people began joining them. Soon a whole crowd was following Jesus.

As the procession came to the top of the hill overlooking Jerusalem, Jesus suddenly stopped the donkey. The shouts of praise and singing in the crowd died away as everyone stopped to look at the view below them.

The wonderful, beloved city of Jerusalem lay before them on the hill of Zion across the Kidron Valley. Some still called it the City of David since King David had been the first one to conquer it and make it the capital of Israel.

But it was the temple that really caught everyone's attention. What a beautiful sight it must have been with its white walls of limestone and marble shining as bright as snow in the afternoon sun.

Now Jesus was talking, and tears were coming to His eyes. Everyone was so surprised. They wondered, "Why would Jesus cry at a time like this?" This was a happy time. Everyone was singing, dancing, and praising God on their way to the city. They were ready to crown Him as the Messiah and King of Israel.

"Oh, Jerusalem! I wish you could always have peace and prosperity such as this," Jesus said. "It is good that you cannot see the days that are coming. One day soon your enemies will surround you, and they will lay siege to this city. Everything will be destroyed! Not one stone will be left standing in your city. Everyone will be killed, even the children, because you did not listen to God who came to live among you."

Jesus knew that the Jewish leaders in Jerusalem had already rejected Him as the Messiah. He was the Son of God, the Redeemer of the world, but they could not see it because they were jealous of His popularity and influence over the people. They had turned their minds over to Satan, and he was the one filling them with so much hate.

At the end of this week, the religious leaders would arrest Him! They would put Him on trial and declare Him guilty of many crimes. They would mock Him, spit on Him, and cruelly whip Him. Some of the people who were in this very procession shouting "Hosanna to the Son of David!" would soon be screaming "Crucify Him!"

Then the procession started up again. Everyone began singing and waving palm branches just as they had before. As they came down the road into Jerusalem, the shouts of praise grew louder, and the gates of the city rang with joy. Jesus was coming into Jerusalem, and they all hoped that He would soon be King!

As the long column came into the city, the people inside asked, "What is all the commotion about?"

The people coming in shouted excitedly, "This is Jesus of Nazareth, the Prophet from Galilee. Blessed is our King who comes in the name of the Lord! Peace in heaven and glory to God in the highest!"

It was a very exciting time for everyone! The words they sang were the same as the ones the angels had sung on the hills surrounding Bethlehem so many years before, when Jesus was born in a manger.

The gates of the city rang with joy. Jesus was coming into Jerusalem, and they all hoped that He would soon be King!

When the Pharisees heard the shouts of praise, they told Jesus, "This is too much noise. Tell everyone to be quiet!"

But Jesus only shook His head. "This is not a time for everyone to be quiet," He said. "If everyone here stopped singing, all the stones in Jerusalem would shout out praises to God!"

So ended the most famous ride by any king in the history of the world. Jesus did not become their king that day, but someday very soon He will come again in the clouds of heaven. When He does, we will crown Him as King of kings and Lord of lords!

Our Prayer:

"Dear Jesus, I want my praises for You to be real. Help me to be faithful to You, even when it is not the popular thing to do."

Hidden Treasure Questions:

- ✔ Why did Jesus ask His disciples to go get a donkey?
- ✔ Why was Jesus sad when He and the people looked at the temple from the Mount of Olives?

Listen to this story online!

Scan for bonus content

A Den of Thieves

This story is taken from Matthew 21, Mark 11, Luke 19, John 2, and *The Desire of Ages*, chapter 65.

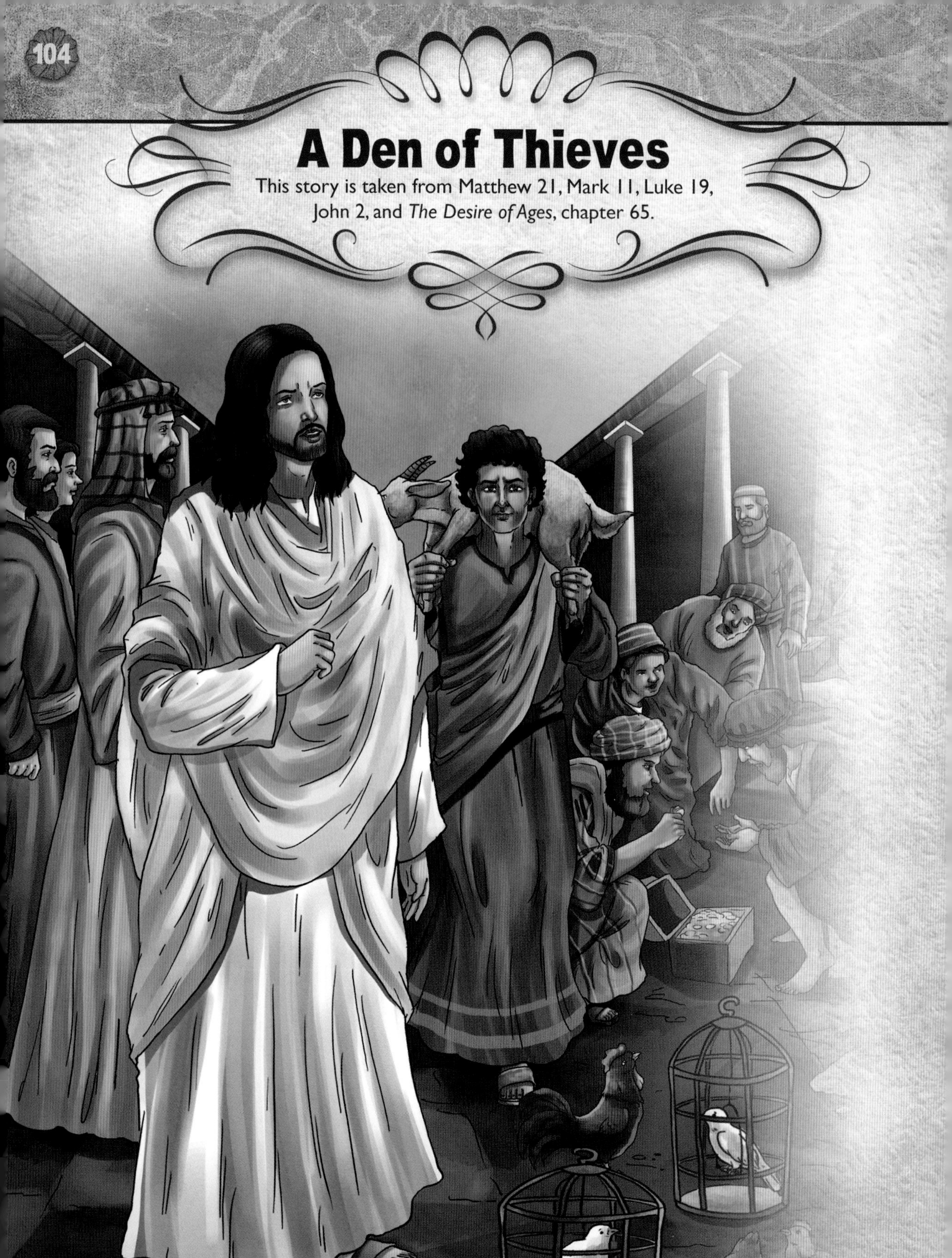

It was Sunday, and Jesus had just arrived in Jerusalem after riding on a donkey all the way from the little town of Bethphage. Thousands had followed Him, waving palm branches and singing hosannas to the Son of David. Everyone had been so excited to see Jesus doing what many rulers did when they were being crowned king in Jerusalem.

Jesus and the disciples now went up to the temple. The crowds followed them as they slowly made their way through the narrow streets of Jerusalem. The Passover Feast would begin in just a few days, and already the city was preparing for the festival. Everyone in the temple would be getting ready for the Jewish holiday too. It was the most exciting time of the year, with music, lights, and good food!

Jesus and His disciples came into the temple court, and they just stopped and looked. The outer court in the temple was filled with people doing business.

Jesus and His disciples came into the temple court, and they just stopped and gasped. The outer court in the temple was filled with people doing business. Merchants and traders were there selling all kinds of things.

Animal pens had been built to hold all the calves, lambs, and goats that people would need for sacrifices in the temple. There were doves and pigeons in cages too for the worshippers who were poor and could not afford the bigger animals. Even food was on sale for people to eat while they did business in the temple market. And, of course, the money changers were there, ready to exchange street money for temple money. That way people could buy the things they would need to worship God.

That upset Jesus the most. The priests and temple leaders were making worship in God's house a business. It was sad, but true. In order to worship God, a man had to have money, even if he was not going to buy an animal for sacrifice. To give an offering, a woman had to take her street money to the exchangers and pay them to exchange it for temple money. Only then could she put the money in the offering box. Street money was considered polluted and unfit for presenting to God.

Jesus, of course, knew that this kind of thing went on all the time. His disciples

Jesus came down the steps and began driving out everyone who was buying and selling in the temple.

should not have been surprised at everything they saw either. They had seen all of this before. Three years before, Jesus had chased the merchants and money changers out of the temple. The temple leaders had been very embarrassed and upset that Jesus would do such a thing.

Now here they were again running the temple like a business, as if God's mercy and grace could be bought for a price. They were charging people money for the privilege of worshipping in God's temple.

As Jesus stood at the top of the temple steps overlooking the courtyard, the noisy crowds began to quiet down. One by one, they caught sight of Him standing there and realized that He was watching them. It seemed as though He was looking into their very souls and was ready to condemn them for what they were doing to God's sacred house.

Many of these people had been in the courtyard three years before, and they remembered seeing Jesus standing in that very same spot. They had seen the anger in His eyes, and now here He was again! Suddenly they felt very guilty and wanted to get as far away from Him as they possibly could!

Jesus' eyes were once again blazing with righteous anger. "It is written in Scripture," He said in trumpetlike tones to the hundreds of people in the temple courtyard, "'My house shall be called a house of prayer for all nations, but you have made it a den of thieves!'"

Then He came down the steps and began driving out everyone who was buying and selling in the temple. Animals were running here and there as He turned over the tables of the money changers and the cages of those who sold doves.

Within a matter of minutes, there was no one left in the temple. All was silent except maybe a few doves that were still flying around.

Now the right kind of people began coming in through the temple gates. The lame, the blind, and the deaf showed up, overjoyed to see Jesus. They came on crutches, on stretchers, and on the backs of their friends. They may not have looked beautiful to the human eye, but to God they looked wonderful. After all, they were His children.

Jesus began healing all those who came to Him, and soon shouts of praise and thanksgiving rang out in the temple courts. Men, women, and children sang God's praises! The old and the young sang "Hosanna to the Son of David!" just as the crowds had done when Jesus was riding the donkey!

When the Pharisees heard the shouts of praise, they once again scolded Jesus and tried to get Him to quiet things down. "The children are making too much noise!" they said impatiently. "Tell them to be quiet!"

But Jesus only shook His head. "Haven't you read the Scripture verses that say, 'The most perfect praise comes from the mouths of babies'?"

Jesus always taught His disciples that unless we become as little children, we will never get into the kingdom of God. Sometimes older people think children should just listen when it is time to worship God, but Jesus did not feel that way at all. He knew that children are very important to the Father in heaven, and He wanted them to sing praises to Him.

But the scribes and chief priests were not happy about any of this. "Does Jesus think He is going to tell us what we should do in our own temple?" they must have asked one another.

Jesus began healing all those who came to Him, and soon shouts of praise and thanksgiving rang out.

Now they really began to talk about how they could get rid of Jesus!

However, they could not just arrest Him in the temple in broad daylight. The common people loved Him too much! He was such a good speaker, and He was always healing people of their diseases. To them, He was a prophet.

If they wanted to kill Him, they were going to have to think of a way to catch Him when no one was around. Maybe they could do it after dark, but when and where? What they needed was someone who knew Jesus well and could tell them where to find Him at night. But the question was, "Who?"

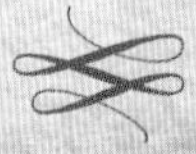

Our Prayer:

"Dear Jesus, I want to be more like You. I want to point people to You so that they can be healed and sing praises to the Father in heaven."

Hidden Treasure Questions:

- ✔ What kinds of people did Jesus drive out of the temple courtyard?
- ✔ After all the people had run out of the courtyard, who came to be healed and sing praises to God?

The Stolen Vineyard

This story is taken from Matthew 21, Mark 12, Luke 20, and *The Desire of Ages*, chapter 65.

The scribes and Pharisees were always trying to get Jesus in trouble. They would come and ask Him trick questions, but Jesus never let them worry Him. He always had an answer that would make them look foolish. Then they would just walk away.

When Jesus was talking to the scribes and Pharisees, He often used parables to make His point. Parables were simple enough for the common person to understand, and yet they were deep enough for the highly educated scribes and Pharisees. The parables were usually quite short and had a simple lesson that Jesus took from their everyday life. One day He told them a parable about a vineyard.

There once was a landowner who planted a vineyard. It took him awhile to get the vineyard going because it takes at least two years for grapevines to produce grapes. Then he built a thorny hedge around the vineyard to keep out robbers and wild animals. Finally, he built a winepress and a watchtower.

When he was finished, the owner

There once was a landowner who planted a vineyard. He built a thorny hedge around the vineyard. Then he built a winepress and a watchtower.

leased the vineyard to vinedressers who would tend it for him. Then he headed off on business to a foreign country.

When the time drew near to harvest the grapes, the landowner sent his servants to the vinedressers so that he might receive his share of the fruit.

However, the vinedressers were a wicked bunch and mistreated the landowner's servants. They beat one of the servants, threw stones at another, and killed a third.

The landowner was angry and sent more servants to collect his crop, but the vinedressers treated them just as badly as they had the first servants.

Finally, the landowner sent his son to the vinedressers. "Surely, they will respect my son," he said.

However, when the vinedressers saw the son, they said, "This is the heir to the vineyard. Come now, let's kill the son, and the vineyard will be ours."

So they took the son and threw him out of the vineyard and killed him.

As Jesus finished His story, He looked around at all the scribes and Pharisees who were listening. "When the owner of the vineyard comes, what do you think he will do to those vinedressers?"

The scribes and Pharisees said, "He will destroy those wicked men and lease his vineyard to other vinedressers who will give him the fruit when it is ready to harvest."

When the chief priests and Pharisees heard this

parable, they realized that Jesus was talking about them. It made them angry, but what could they do? They could not arrest Him right then and there. They were afraid of the crowds because everybody thought of Jesus as a prophet.

Jesus had told the story about the wicked vinedressers because He wanted the Pharisees to see themselves for who they really were. Like the wicked vinedressers, the Jewish nation had not been kind to the prophets and other messengers that God had sent them. They had persecuted them and even killed some of them. John the Baptist was a perfect example. They hated him, and would have killed him if Herod had not done it first.

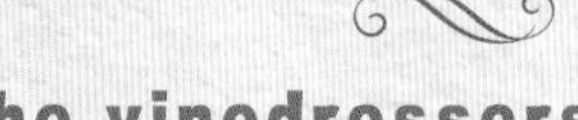

The vinedressers were a wicked bunch. They beat one of the servants, threw stones at another, and killed a third.

Now they planned to kill Jesus, too. This parable told the religious leaders that Jesus knew exactly what they were going to do, but that did not stop them. Already they were planning when and how they would arrest Him. Very soon they would put Him on trial, and then execute Him as a criminal.

But, of course, the death of Jesus was part of God's plan for the salvation of the world, and Jesus was the One to see that the plan was carried out.

Our Prayer:

"Dear Jesus, help me to be faithful in all the jobs You want me to do for You."

Hidden Treasure Questions:

- ✔ What was the parable about that Jesus told the scribes and Pharisees?
- ✔ Who was Jesus talking about in the parable? In other words, whom was the parable really meant for?

Listen to this story online!

Scan for bonus content

Sheep and Goats

This story is taken from Matthew 25.

Jesus knew that it was almost time for Him to die on the cross, but He was already looking forward to the day when He would come back to earth the second time. He said there would be only two groups of people when He came again in the clouds of heaven. They would be the good and the bad, the righteous and the wicked. There would be no in-betweens. Jesus said that when that time came, many would be very happy to see Him. However, others would be surprised at the way things turned out for them.

"When the Son of Man comes in His glory, and all the holy angels with Him, then He will sit on the throne of His glory," Jesus said. "In that day when everyone is being judged for all the good or evil they have done, all the nations of the earth will be gathered before Him. Then Jesus will separate the good people from the bad as a shepherd divides his sheep from the goats. And He will set the sheep on His right hand, but the goats will be on the left."

Jesus said, "In that day when everyone is being judged. He will set the sheep on His right hand, but the goats will be on the left."

This was a very interesting illustration for Jesus to use as a parable. In His day, shepherds kept herds of sheep and goats. Sheep and goats were raised for their meat and milk, or for their wool, hair, or hides. Sheep and goats were a sign of wealth. Both were very valuable, and the more of them a man had, the richer he was considered.

Now, sheep are gentle animals. They are timid and easily frightened and do not seem to be very smart. They need protection and a safe place to sleep each night. However, they tend to be followers. Goats, on the other hand, tend to be noisy and stubborn. They are bold and do not seem to be afraid of anything. They will go anywhere, anytime, and will eat just about anything.

In this parable, Jesus was comparing people to sheep and goats. After all, some people are a lot like sheep, while some are more like goats.

In the day of judgment that is coming, King Jesus will say to the sheep on His right hand, "Come, everyone who is blessed by My Father, inherit the kingdom prepared for you from the foundation of the world. For I was hungry and you gave Me food. I was thirsty and you gave Me drink. I was a stranger and you took Me in. I had no clothes and you gave Me some. I was sick and you visited Me. I was in prison and you came to visit Me."

Then the righteous will answer Him, "Lord, when did we see You hungry and feed You, or thirsty and give You a drink? When did we see You as a stranger and give You a place to stay, or without clothes and give You some? Or when did we see You sick, or in prison, and come to visit You?"

The King will answer them, "Just as you did all these things for those who think they are the least important in My kingdom, you did them for Me."

However, the King will have much harsher words for the goats on His left hand. "Depart from Me, you cursed ones, into everlasting fire prepared for the devil and his angels. For I was hungry and you gave Me no food. I was thirsty and you gave Me nothing to drink. I was a stranger and you did not take Me in. I had no clothes and you gave Me none. I was sick and in prison and you didn't visit Me."

"Just as you did all these things for those who think they are the least important in My kingdom, you did them for Me."

Then they will say to the King, "Lord, when did we see You hungry, or thirsty, or a stranger with no clothes, or sick, or in prison, and did not help You?"

Then the King will answer them, "Just as you did not do any of these things for those who are the least important in My kingdom, you didn't do them for Me." Then these wicked ones will go away into everlasting punishment, but the righteous will receive eternal life.

If you and I were to find our place in this parable, where would we be? With the sheep or with the goats? One day very soon, Jesus will come again, and then He will separate the sheep from the goats. That will be a very exciting day if we are the sheep Jesus was talking about. Let's plan on it.

Our Prayer:

"Dear Jesus, help me to be kind to those who need help."

Hidden Treasure Questions:

- ✔ Whom do the sheep and goats represent?
- ✔ When Jesus comes again, what will He say to those who have helped others?

Look for My Return

This story is taken from Matthew 24, Mark 13, Luke 21, and *The Desire of Ages*, chapter 69.

Jesus knew that hard times were coming for His disciples. He knew that after He died, arose again from the dead, and went back to heaven, the church would suffer persecution from Satan. The enemies of Jesus and the church would try to destroy the Christians and all that they would do for God.

The nation of Israel was in trouble too. The Jews were rejecting Jesus as the Savior of the world, and they would persecute the Christians, putting many to death. Because of this, God would soon reject them as His chosen people. Without God's blessing, they would have no protection from their enemies, and in just a few years, the Romans would destroy Jerusalem.

On Jesus' last day in the temple before His death, He had only words of doom for the Jewish leaders. They did not want to hear His words of life, and now there was nothing left for Him to say except, "Behold, your house is left unto you desolate!" In other words, this magnificent temple was their house now, not God's house, and it would soon be destroyed.

Jesus pointed to the buildings. "Do you see all this?" He told His disciples. "Soon not one stone here will be left standing on another. Everything will be torn down."

"Tell us, when will these things be?" the disciples asked. "And what will be the sign of Your coming, and of the end of the age?"

Later, when He was alone, Peter, James, John, and Andrew came to Him as He sat upon the Mount of Olives. "Tell us, when will these things be?" they asked. "And what will be the sign of Your coming, and of the end of the age?"

Jesus knew that it would be hard for His disciples to hear all the bad things that were going to happen to their nation, but they needed to know the signs that would show them when His coming was near.

"Soon the end will come for the city of Jerusalem and all Judea, too," Jesus said. "When you see Jerusalem surrounded by armies, then know that the time for its destruction is near. Those who are still in Judea at that time should flee to the mountains.

"Those who are in Jerusalem must also leave immediately, and those who are in the fields and small towns should not go back to the city. Do not try to go back to your home to take anything with you, and pray that you don't have to flee during the winter or on the Sabbath," Jesus said.

"You will hear of wars and rumors that wars are coming. Nations will fight against each other, and kingdoms will fight other kingdoms. There will be famines, pestilences, and earthquakes in various places.

"Everything I am telling you must come to pass, but the end is not yet. Men's hearts will fail them for fear of all those things that are coming on the earth. Crimes will be committed everywhere, and people will betray each other because there will be more hate than love in the world.

"Then there will be a great time of trouble," Jesus told them. "It will be like nothing the world has ever seen. Times will be hard, and unless God shortens those days, no one will be saved; but for the chosen ones' sake, those days will be shortened.

"You will hear of wars and rumors that wars are coming."

"They will lay their hands on you and persecute you, and you will be hated by all nations for the sake of the gospel. They will deliver you up to the synagogues and prisons. You will be brought before kings and rulers for My name's sake. However, it will turn out for you as an occasion for testimony. Therefore, settle it in your hearts not to meditate beforehand on what you will answer. For I will give you the words and wisdom that all your adversaries will not be able to contradict or resist. Even parents, brothers, relatives, and friends will betray you, and they will put some of you to death. And you will be hated by all for My name's sake.

"There will also be signs in the sky that Jesus' coming is near. In the years just following the time of great persecution, the sun will be darkened, the moon will not give its light, and the stars will fall from heaven.

"False christs and false prophets will show up and do wonders to deceive, if possible, even the elect. I have given you fair warning before it happens, so that when it happens, your faith will become stronger. If someone tells you 'The Messiah is in the desert,' do not go out. If anyone says He is hiding somewhere, do not believe them. The coming of the Son of Man will be like lightning that flashes from the east all the way to the west.

"When it is time for Me to come, a small cloud will appear in the east. And all the tribes of the earth will mourn when they see the Son of Man coming in the clouds of heaven with power and great glory. He will send His angels with a trumpet call, and they will gather together His faithful ones from one end of the earth to the other.

"But the day and the hour of His coming no one knows," Jesus said, "not even the angels of heaven, but My Father only.

"For this gospel of the kingdom must be preached to every nation in the world, and then the end will come.

"As it was in the days of Noah, so will it be at the coming of the Son of Man. During the days before the flood, they were eating, drinking, and marrying, until the day that Noah went into the ark. They knew nothing about it until the flood came and washed them all away. It will be just like that before the Son of Man comes again. So be ready, for the Son of Man is coming at an hour that you don't expect Him. Those who are faithful to the end will be saved.

"For this gospel of the kingdom must be preached to every nation in the world, and then the end will come."

"Now, when these things begin to happen, look up and lift up your heads because your redemption draws near."

Jesus knew that these times would be very difficult for His followers. Satan hates all of us as much as he hates God, and he wants us to give up our faith in the promises of the Bible. He wants us to doubt that Jesus will ever come again. But Jesus has promised, "Be faithful until death, and I will give you the crown of life" (Revelation 2:10).

Our Prayer:

"Dear Jesus, help me to recognize the signs of Your coming, and help me to be ready for that very important day."

Hidden Treasure Questions:

- ✔ What was one of the signs that Jerusalem was going to be destroyed?
- ✔ What are some of the signs that Jesus is coming again?

Listen to this story online!

Scan for bonus content

The Hidden Money

This story is taken from Matthew 25 and Luke 19.

One of Jesus' favorite things to talk about with His disciples was the kingdom of God. More than anything Jesus wants us to spend forever with Him in that kingdom. God has given each one of us special abilities so that we can have a part in leading our friends and neighbors to Christ. Then they can enjoy heaven too. The story of the 10 talents is to show that each of us has a responsibility to use our special abilities in service for Him.

Jesus said, "The kingdom of heaven is like a businessman who traveled to a far country. Before he left, he called his servants and divided his money (or talents, as they were called) among them to use in expanding his business while he was gone.

"The master gave five talents to one servant, two talents to another, and one talent to a third. Each servant received what they should have according to their abilities. Then the master left on his journey.

"The servant who received five talents started a business. He went right to work. He bought, sold, and traded, using the five talents that the master had given him, and he made another five talents. The servant who had received two talents also went right to work. He took his two talents and traded them wisely, and his hard work paid off. He made two more talents.

"However, the servant who had received one talent did nothing with his money. He didn't go to work like the others. He took the money outside, dug a hole in the ground, and buried his master's money.

"After a long time, the master of those servants came home and called his servants in to settle his financial accounts with them.

"The master addressed the servant who had received five talents by saying, 'I gave you five talents. Give me a report of how you invested my money.' The servant responded, 'Lord, you did give me five talents to work with, and look, I have made five more talents besides the ones I was given.'

"The master was very pleased with the first servant. 'Well done, my good and faithful servant,' he said. 'You were faithful over a few things, and now I will put you in charge of many things. Join me as we celebrate your success.'

"The master then turned to the servant who had received two talents and said, 'What have you done with the two talents I gave you?' The servant humbly said, 'Lord, you gave me two talents to work with, and look, I have made two more talents besides the ones I was given.'

"The master smiled at the second servant's report and said, 'Well done, good and faithful servant. You have been faithful over a few things, so now I will let you manage many things. Join me as we celebrate your success.'

"Now it was time for the servant who had been given the one talent to give his report. He was afraid because he knew that he had nothing good to say. So before the master could even ask for a report, the servant stammered, 'Lord, I knew you to be a hard man. I know that you are strict and often want something from nothing.

The servant who had received one talent said, "I was afraid and hid your talent in the ground."

Even when you haven't planted a crop, you sometimes expect a harvest. So I was afraid and hid your talent in the ground, but look, I still have the same amount you gave me. Here, take what is yours.'

"The master was very angry. 'You wicked and lazy servant!' he said. 'You are right. I do sometimes expect something from nothing, maybe even when I haven't planted a crop. In that case, you should have at least put my money in the bank so that when I came I could receive it with interest.'

"'Now take that talent from this servant and give it to him who has 10 talents,' he told his steward. And with that the master threw the lazy servant out the back door into the night."

"You wicked and lazy servant!" he said. "You should have at least put my money in the bank."

What is the lesson for us in this parable? God is a Good Master who has given us the privilege of working with Him to save souls. Some have good speaking talents or abilities, some have singing abilities, and others have been blessed with medical abilities. All of these abilities can be used to glorify God. Some of us have the gift of kindness that draws others to us, and then we can share our testimony with them. The list of God's gifts goes on and on.

The point is that each of us has received at least one special gift. We should use that gift to please Jesus. If we don't, we will be like the lazy servant who showed that he had no respect for what he had received by burying his gift and doing absolutely nothing.

I want to do my best to use the talents God has given me to bless others and to lead them to Jesus. Don't you?

Our Prayer:

"Dear Father, help me to be faithful in all the little jobs that I do so that I can be faithful in the big jobs."

Hidden Treasure Questions:

- ✔ How many servants did the master have?
- ✔ What did each servant do with the money that the master gave him?

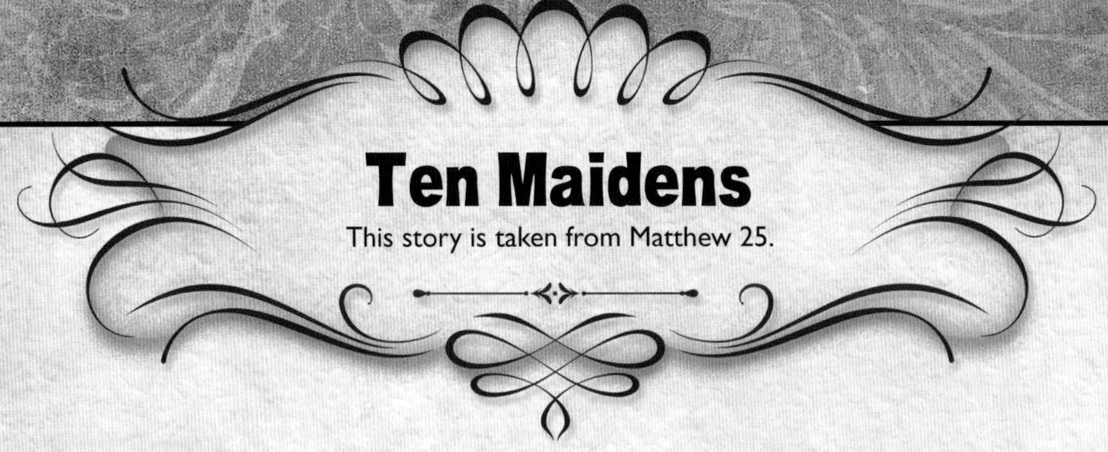

Ten Maidens

This story is taken from Matthew 25.

Jesus told the story of 10 young maidens who were asked to be part of a wedding party and carry oil lamps to light the way. The lamps were made of hardened clay and fit nicely into the palm of their hand. Olive oil was poured into the lamps, and a small wick was then put into each lamp to float on top of the oil. If a wick was trimmed properly, when lit it could burn quite brightly. If there were lots of these lamps, the road or pathway that the wedding party traveled would be nicely lit.

Now, the story says that five of the young maidens got ready for the big event by bringing extra oil with them. That way, if they ran out, they could always refill their lamps. However, five of the maidens did not bring extra oil. The five who brought extra oil were called wise, and the five who did not were called foolish. Here is why.

Unfortunately, the wedding did not get started as soon as everyone thought it would. In those days, weddings didn't start at a specific time like the ones you see on the printed invitations we get in the mail today. They started when everyone was ready.

Now, if a bride isn't ready, the wedding doesn't begin. But in those days it was sometimes more about the groom, since he had to make all the preparations for the wedding, and the feast that would follow.

Ten young maidens were asked to be part of the wedding party and carry oil lamps to light the way.

Anyway, in the story Jesus told, it got dark, and the young maidens lit their oil lamps, thinking that the groom would soon arrive. But he did not. Everybody waited and waited for the groom to get there, but still he didn't come. In the meantime, it got very late. So late, in fact, that the young maidens waiting to lead the wedding party dozed off. The lamps they were holding went out because all their oil had burned up.

Then at midnight, a messenger came running through the streets shouting, "The bridegroom is coming! Get up, everyone, and go out to meet him!"

The 10 young maidens jumped up to join the wedding party, but discovered that their lamps had gone out. So everyone trimmed the wicks in their lamps, but since they had no oil, the lamps couldn't be lit.

The five wise maidens poured the extra oil that they had brought with them into their lamps, but the five foolish maidens had no extra oil. "Please share some of your oil with us," they begged.

"We can't do that," said the five wise maidens. "If we give you some of our oil, we won't have enough for ourselves. You had better go try to buy some."

So the foolish maidens ran off to find some oil, but all the shops were closed at that hour. While they were gone, the groom arrived to get his bride. The wedding procession then left to begin its way back down the street. When the wedding party arrived at the groom's house, everyone went in, and the door was shut.

Meanwhile, the five foolish maidens were still looking for oil, and when they arrived at the groom's house, the door was shut and locked.

"We are here!" the five foolish maidens called to the doorman of the feast. "Let us in!"

But the man guarding the door shook his head. "I am sorry," he said. "I don't know you!"

The foolish maidens ran off to find some oil, but all the shops were closed.

This story shows us the importance of making plans for emergencies in life. Even more important, it warns us that we need to be ready to meet Jesus when He comes the second time.

Many people today are discouraged as they wait for Jesus to come again. They are sometimes tempted to think He will never come. But He will! Like the groom in our story, He has to! He is already engaged to us because we are His church!

When we give our hearts to Jesus, it is as if we are engaged to Him. The church is the bride of Christ. We are engaged to go to heaven to live with Him forever and ever. He will come back for us. The only thing that we need to worry about is how much oil we have on hand.

The oil in the lamps represents the Holy Spirit. The Holy Spirit can be doing wonderful things in our lives, but if we don't get a new supply every morning, we will run out.

Let's all plan to be wise like the five maidens who had an extra supply of oil with them at all times. Let's be watching and waiting faithfully for Jesus to come, because we don't know exactly when that will be.

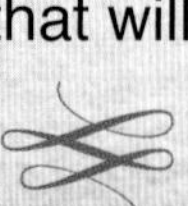

Our Prayer:

"Dear Father, help me to always have an extra supply of the Holy Spirit in my life."

Hidden Treasure Questions:

✔ How many young maidens were asked to lead the wedding party?

✔ Why did the doorkeeper not let the five foolish maidens come into the wedding feast?

Scan for bonus content

First Communion

This story is taken from Matthew 26, Mark 14, Luke 22, John 13, and *The Desire of Ages*, chapters 71 and 72.

It was time for the Passover feast, but Jesus and His disciples had no place to celebrate the special meal. Then Jesus called Peter and John to His side. "Go and prepare the Passover for us that we may eat," He told them.

"Do you have someplace in mind?" they asked.

Jesus said to them, "When you go into the city, you will meet a man carrying a pitcher of water. Follow him into the house where he is going. Then you shall say to the master of the house, 'Our Teacher is asking for the guest room. His time is at hand. He will keep the Passover at your house with His disciples.' Then he will show you a large, furnished upper room. Make preparations for the meal there."

So Peter and John went on ahead and found everything just as Jesus had said it would be. There they prepared the Passover meal.

When it was evening, Jesus and the 12 disciples all came together to eat the Passover in the upper room. "This is a very special evening," Jesus told everyone. "Before My time of suffering begins, I want to eat the Passover with you one more time. I won't be eating it again until we come together in the kingdom of heaven."

Then Jesus said, "The one who will betray Me is here at the table with Me tonight. It was prophesied that the Son of Man must die, but cursed is the one who betrays Him."

The disciples were all alarmed when they heard this, and they began to ask one another who would do such a thing.

When the meal was over, Jesus got up from the table and began to wash the disciples' feet.

When He came to Peter, Peter said to Him, "Why are You washing my feet, Lord?"

Jesus said, "Maybe you can't understand what I am doing for you here tonight, but one day you will."

Peter shook his head. "You shall never wash my feet!"

"If I don't wash your feet, you will have no part in My kingdom," Jesus replied.

Peter bowed his head humbly. "Lord, wash everything then. Not just my feet, but also my hands and my head!"

When Jesus had finished washing all their feet, He said, "You have seen Me wash your feet, and now I want you to follow My example. Wash one another's feet."

Then Jesus took bread and broke it and gave it to them to pass around. "This bread represents My body, which is given for you," He said. "Eat it in remembrance of Me."

Then He took a cup of grape juice and gave thanks to His heavenly Father for it. Afterward He passed it around to the disciples. "Take this and drink from it," He said. "This cup of juice represents My blood, which I

When it was evening, Jesus and the 12 disciples all came together to eat the Passover in the upper room.

will shed for you. It is My new covenant with you. From this day forward, I won't be drinking any grape juice until I come again the second time."

Now Jesus began to be very sad and spoke of His betrayer again.

So John leaned back and asked Jesus plainly, "Lord, who is it?" and everyone after him also asked, "Is it I, Lord?"

Judas also asked Jesus the question, and Jesus said, "It is he to whom I shall give a piece of bread when I have dipped it in the dish." And having dipped the bread, He immediately gave it to Judas Iscariot.

Then He said to Judas, "Whatever you are going to do, do it quickly." No one at the table knew what Jesus meant when He told Judas to "do it quickly."

Judas got up and went out immediately into the night.

After he left, Jesus said, "A new commandment I give to you, that you love one another; as I have loved you, that you also love one another. By this, all will know that you are My disciples."

Jesus' example of washing feet is a beautiful symbol that we celebrate to show that He has washed away our sins.

As Jesus said, the bread represents His body offered for you and me on the cross. The juice represents His blood.

Many churches do this in a special ceremony called the ordinance of humility, or sometimes called the foot-washing ceremony. We do it because Jesus asked us to do it. It is a very humbling experience, and Jesus knew that. He knew that if we are willing to wash another person's feet, we would be willing to do just about anything for them.

We also have a ceremony called Communion in which we eat bread and drink grape juice. As Jesus said, the bread represents His body offered for you and me on the cross. The juice represents His blood shed for you and me when He died. When we take part in this ceremony, we are saying that we accept Jesus' sacrifice for us. Isn't that a wonderful gift that Jesus gave us?

Our Prayer:

"Dear Jesus, thank You for giving us the symbols of grape juice and bread to represent Your death for us."

Hidden Treasure Questions:

- ✔ Which two disciples prepared the Passover meal?
- ✔ What did Jesus do for His disciples the night of the Passover feast to wash away their sins?

Listen to this story online!

Scan for bonus content

A Terrible Night in the Garden

This story is taken from Matthew 26, Mark 14, Luke 22, John 14, and *The Desire of Ages*, chapters 73 and 74.

Jesus and His disciples had spent the evening in the upper room celebrating the Passover. Jesus had washed the disciples' feet, introducing a new Christian ceremony called the foot-washing service.

Then He introduced another part of that ceremony called Communion. This ceremony included bread, which represented the body of Christ, and grape juice, which represented His blood that would be shed for you and me. Jesus passed the bread and grape juice around for the disciples to eat and drink.

While in the upper room, Jesus talked about the promises of eternal life. He told them, "Let not your heart be troubled; you believe in God, believe also in Me. In My Father's house are many mansions; if it were not so, I would have told you. I go to prepare a place for you. And if I go and prepare a place for you, I will come again and receive you to Myself; that where I am, there you may be also."

However, the disciples did not understand. They said, "Lord, we do not know where You are going, so how can we know the way?"

Jesus was surprised that the disciples would ask such questions after all the time that He had been with them. "I am the way, the truth, and the life," He said. "No one comes to the Father except through Me."

As Jesus shared these promises with His disciples, a glorious light from heaven shone on His face. The disciples stared at Jesus in awe and grew quiet as they realized that the angels must be near.

"I have many things I would like to tell you," Jesus said, "but you will not understand them right now. However, when the Holy Spirit comes upon you, He will guide you into all truth, and He will show you things to come."

Jesus talked about many things. "I am the vine; you are the branches," He told them.

Then Jesus and His disciples all sang a song and left the upper room to go to the Garden of Gethsemane on the Mount of Olives for the evening.

As they walked along, Jesus talked about many things because this was the last time He would be with them before He died. "I am the vine; you are the branches," He told them. "If you are attached to Me like the vines of a grapevine, then your life will be a witness for Me. And you will bear fruit for Me."

Jesus was very sad, but His disciples did not understand why. They did not know that in just a few hours He would be dragged off to a trial to suffer at the hands of evil men. They did not know that He would be mocked, beaten, and then crucified on a cross.

Jesus had tried to warn His disciples about what was coming, but the last few weeks they had been arguing a lot about who would get the best jobs in the coming kingdom.

He had told them again and again that His kingdom would not be like an earthly one. It would not be established by overthrowing the Romans with force. God's kingdom would be established by loving your neighbor as yourself, putting others first, and being kind. Those who would be in Christ's kingdom would have to strive to be like Christ in character. Christ spent a lot of time telling His disciples this, but they just could not understand it.

"Oh, My Father," He prayed, "if it is possible, take this cup of suffering from Me."

When Jesus and the disciples reached the Garden of Gethsemane on the Mount of Olives, He said to them, "Pray that you may not enter into temptation."

Then He went on a little farther, taking Peter, James, and John with Him. "I am so overwhelmed with sadness that I feel as if I could die," He said with a heavy heart. "Stay here and watch with Me."

These three disciples had often come to this spot in the garden with Jesus at night. While He prayed, they would sleep a little ways from their Master until He came to wake them up again in the morning. Tonight it was different. He wanted them to spend the night with Him in prayer.

Leaving the three disciples to pray, Jesus went still farther into the garden to pray by Himself.

The three disciples watched Him go. They wondered, "What is wrong with Him?" They had never seen Him so sad before! It looked as if the weight of the world was on His shoulders, and it was! The sins of everyone who had ever lived on earth were being put on Jesus that night.

Meanwhile, Jesus had fallen on His face to the ground in prayer. "Oh, My Father," He prayed, "if it is possible, take this cup of suffering from Me. Nevertheless, not as I will, but as You will!"

Jesus was in great agony as He prayed for help from the Father. He was under such stress that He began to sweat drops of blood. Satan wanted to discourage Jesus. He wanted Jesus to give up the idea of dying for the sins of the world and go back to heaven.

After praying for a while, Jesus got up, went back to the three disciples, and found them sound asleep. Waking Peter, He said, "Peter, are you sleeping? Couldn't you watch with Me one hour? Watch and pray, or else you may be tempted. The spirit indeed is willing, but the flesh is weak."

Then He went away to pray a second time. "Oh, My Father," He prayed, "if this cup cannot pass from Me unless I drink it, Your will be done." The war between good and evil was being fought there in the Garden of Gethsemane, and Jesus knew that prayer was His only hope. He might not want to go through with heaven's plan for Him to die for the world, but He was willing to do it if that is what had to be done.

Later Jesus went back to His disciples and found them asleep again. He tried to wake them up, but their eyes were heavy, and they could not stay awake.

Again, He went back into the garden to pray alone. By now, Jesus was getting very weak. "Please, Father," He prayed, "do not ask Me to go through with this. I do not want to die. However, I will trust You to do whatever is best."

Then He fainted and collapsed on the ground. Suddenly a bright light shone around Him, and an angel appeared from heaven to give Him strength and courage. If the angel hadn't come to His rescue, Jesus would have died right there in the garden.

When He returned to the disciples, He found them still asleep.

Jesus had finished praying. He was ready to meet whatever Satan would bring Him in the hours to come. When He returned to the disciples, He found them still asleep. "You have been sleeping long enough," He said, waking them up. "The Son of Man has been betrayed into the hands of sinners. Get up! It is time to go. See, My betrayer is here already."

Our Prayer:

"Dear Jesus, thank You for making the decision to die for my sins. I can never repay You, but I will give You my heart."

Hidden Treasure Questions:

- Which three disciples did Jesus take with Him into the Garden of Gethsemane?
- How many times did Jesus go away to pray that night?

Listen to this story online!

Scan for bonus content

Judas Betrays Jesus

This story is taken from Matthew 26, Mark 14, Luke 22, John 18, and *The Desire of Ages*, chapter 74.

The disciples awoke with a start.

"It's time to go!" Jesus said, shaking the disciples to wake them up. "See, My betrayer is here already."

Sure enough, as the disciples all crowded around Jesus, they could see a line of lights coming up through the garden. While Jesus was still speaking, a mob with swords, clubs, and lanterns arrived and surrounded Him. The chief priests and elders of the temple were there too, with some temple guards. Leading them all was Judas.

The disciples were terrified, but Jesus didn't seem surprised at all. He knew exactly what was going to happen and stepped forward now. "Whom are you seeking?" He said.

"Jesus of Nazareth," said the priests.

"I am He," Jesus replied.

Suddenly the angel who had come to encourage Jesus in the garden stepped between Him and the mob. A heavenly light flashed across Jesus' face, and a light in the form of a dove hovered over Him.

At sight of this heavenly glory, the mob staggered back. Priests, elders, soldiers, and even Judas fell to the ground as though they were dead men.

Then the light faded away just as quickly as it had come. Jesus could have escaped, but He did not.

The disciples were stunned by what they saw, but no one made a move.

"Whom are you seeking?" Jesus asked again.

"Jesus of Nazareth," the priests repeated.

"I have told you already that I am Jesus. So if you are looking for Me, let these men go." He pointed to His disciples.

Judas now stepped forward. He had given the temple guards a sign, telling them, "The Man I kiss is the one you want. Seize Him, and lead Him away."

Judas walked up to Jesus and said, "Greetings, Rabbi!" and then kissed Him on the cheek. This was how friends greeted each other in those days.

But Jesus wasn't impressed. "Judas, are you betraying the Son of Man with a kiss?" He asked.

While Jesus was still speaking, a mob with swords, clubs, and lanterns arrived and surrounded Him. Leading them all was Judas.

Then the temple guards surrounded Jesus again, and the disciples now realized that this was a trap to catch Jesus. "Lord, shall we strike with the sword?" they shouted, and Peter, who had a sword, pulled it out. Swinging it with all his might, he cut off the right ear of Malchus, the high priest's servant.

Immediately, Jesus freed His hands and reached out to heal Malchus' ear. Then He turned to Peter. "Put your sword into its sheath, Peter. All who take the sword will perish by the sword. Don't you think that I could now pray to My Father, and He would provide Me with more than 12 legions of angels? But it is not to be," He added. "I must drink the cup that My Father has given Me. If I don't, then how can the prophecies of Scripture be fulfilled that I should save the world?"

Jesus then turned to the chief priests, the captains of the temple guard, and the elders who had all come out to capture Him. “Am I a robber that you have to come after Me with swords and clubs?” He said. “I was with you every day teaching in the temple, and you never tried to arrest Me then. But I am not surprised. This is your hour when you have the power of darkness on your side.”

Immediately, Jesus freed His hands and reached out to heal Malchus' ear. Then He turned to Peter and said, "Put your sword away."

Now the mob surrounded Jesus again, grabbing at Him to tie His hands. When they realized that He was finally in their power, they began punching and shoving Him.

Jesus did not fight back. He just let them take Him away.

The disciples began to really panic now. What was Jesus doing? Why was He letting the mob treat Him this way? Things were not supposed to go like this! Where was the angel who had been here just a few minutes before? Why wasn't Jesus letting His disciples fight for Him?

It was a moment of desperation for all of them, but one thing was sure. If Jesus was not going to save Himself, and He wasn't going to let them help Him, there was nothing more they could do here now. And with that, all of the disciples abandoned Jesus and fled into the darkness.

Our Prayer:

"Dear Jesus, I wish I could have been in the garden with You the night You were betrayed. I would have prayed with You."

Hidden Treasure Questions:

- ✔ Who came to the garden to arrest Jesus?
- ✔ Why did Judas kiss Jesus?

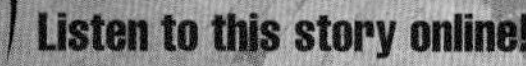

Listen to this story online!

Scan for bonus content

Trial Before Annas and Caiaphas

This story is taken from Matthew 26, Mark 14, Luke 22, John 18, and *The Desire of Ages*, chapter 75.

The worst night of Jesus' life on earth had come. The temple guards dragged Him from the garden tied up like a common criminal. Now and then one of the guards would slap Him or kick Him, and if He tripped and fell, they yanked Him to His feet again along the rough stony pathway.

Down the road from the garden they led Him, through the Kidron Valley and in through the gates to the city. First, they led Him to the house of Annas because his son-in-law, Caiaphas, was high priest that year. Annas was the ex-high priest and was still head of the priestly family.

Down the road from the garden they led Him to the house of Annas.

"Tell us about Your disciples and some of the things You taught them," Annas said as he and his council began their interrogation of Jesus.

"I spoke openly to the world," Jesus replied. "I always taught in synagogues and in the temple, where the Jews meet every day. I have never said anything in secret. Why don't you ask the elders here tonight what I have taught? They know what I said."

One of the temple officers walked up to Jesus and slapped Him on the face. "Is that the way You answer a high priest?" he demanded.

"If I have said something wrong, then punish Me for that," Jesus said, "but if not, why hit Me?"

Before long Annas realized that they were not getting anywhere in their questioning, so he ordered that Jesus be taken to the house of Caiaphas. By the time they arrived, it was early morning and very dark. There was a group of Jewish leaders waiting in the judgment hall to have a secret council about Jesus.

The midnight arrest, as well as the mockery and abuse of Jesus before He was condemned, or even accused, were against the law. Their own laws declared that men should be treated as innocent until proven guilty. Holding a trial at night was also illegal, but they did it anyway.

However, they did not call certain members of the council such as Nicodemus and Joseph of Arimathea, because by their own rules the priests stood condemned. They remembered when Nicodemus had said, "Does our law judge a man before it hears him and knows what he is doing?" They did not want either Nicodemus or Joseph of Arimathea to speak in favor of justice.

Almost immediately the trial started. They were trying to find something Jesus had said or done that would make Him a guilty criminal in their eyes. And if the crime was big enough, they could then have Him executed.

The chief priests called in many witnesses in hopes of finding someone who would give false testimony against Jesus. However, when the witnesses were cross-examined, none of them could agree on what Jesus had done. Soon everyone in the meeting was arguing and fighting.

Finally, two false witnesses came forward to tell the same story about something that they had heard Jesus say. "This fellow told us, 'I am able to destroy the temple of God and build it in three days,'" they said.

It was not true, of course, because the witnesses were misquoting Him, but Jesus did not say a thing to defend Himself.

Then the high priest stood up. "Aren't You going to say anything?" he demanded. "Are these men telling the truth about You?" But Jesus still would not talk.

The high priest realized that if he could not get Jesus to talk, he would not be able to get Him to say anything they could use against Him.

Finally, in desperation, the high priest said to Jesus, “Tell us under oath before God, are You the Christ and the Son of God?”

Jesus said to him, “It is true just as you have said, and one day soon you will see the Son of Man sitting at the right hand of God coming in the clouds of heaven.”

The high priest tore his robe. "He is guilty of death!"

When the high priest heard this, he tore his robe. “This Man has spoken blasphemy!” he shouted. “Why do we need any more witnesses? Look, now you have heard the blasphemy from His own mouth! What do you think?”

“He is guilty of death!” they all said, and then they spit on Jesus and began to beat Him. One of the temple officers put a blindfold on Him and slapped Him across the face. “Prophesy to us!” he shouted. “Tell us the name of the man who hit You just now!”

It was a horrible night. Satan was doing everything he could to make Jesus give up and go back to heaven! Jesus had come to show the Jews the love of the Father. He had come to bring them eternal life, and this was how they treated Him?

It was all very hard for the angels of God to watch. So painful was it that they all finally had to turn away in sadness.

Our Prayer:

"Dear Jesus, I'm sorry that the people all treated You so badly at Your trial. I pray that I will be as faithful to the Father as You were."

Hidden Treasure Questions:

- ✔ What was the name of the high priest in Jerusalem?
- ✔ What did Jesus say that made everyone think that He was guilty?

Listen to this story online!

Scan for bonus content

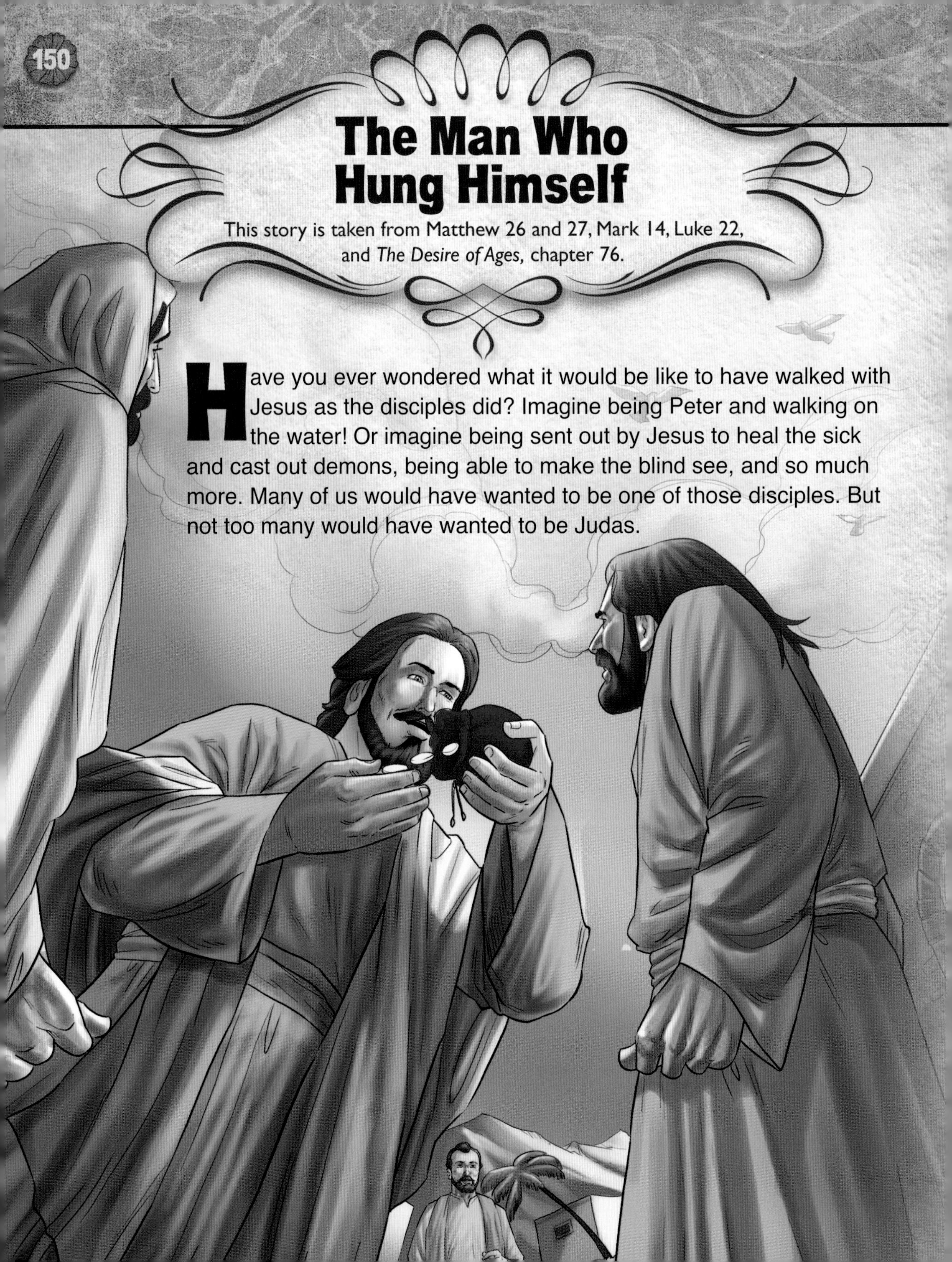

The Man Who Hung Himself

This story is taken from Matthew 26 and 27, Mark 14, Luke 22, and *The Desire of Ages*, chapter 76.

Have you ever wondered what it would be like to have walked with Jesus as the disciples did? Imagine being Peter and walking on the water! Or imagine being sent out by Jesus to heal the sick and cast out demons, being able to make the blind see, and so much more. Many of us would have wanted to be one of those disciples. But not too many would have wanted to be Judas.

Judas was a talented man, and quite smart. When he became a disciple of Jesus, he was a leader from the start.

Judas became the treasurer, so he was the one in charge of the money bag that held the donations people gave to Jesus. His intelligence and desire to be a disciple were good things, but there was a problem.

The outward appearance of Judas looked good. But the inside was a different story. He was a selfish man, proud and dishonest. Though the other disciples did not know about it, he sometimes would steal money from the money bag.

Judas wanted Jesus to become the king of Israel. If Jesus really was the Messiah, as He claimed He was, why was He waiting so long to set Himself up as king over Israel? He decided to force Jesus into becoming king and settle the issue forever. He decided he would deliver Jesus to the priests, and that would force Him to establish His kingdom.

For 30 pieces of silver, Judas agreed to show the temple priests the spot where Jesus usually went to pray alone at night.

If his plan worked, Judas would get the credit and be promoted to one of the most important positions in the kingdom. In addition, he would be 30 pieces of silver richer. What a great plan, he thought.

For 30 pieces of silver, Judas agreed to show the temple priests the spot where Jesus usually went to pray alone at night.

But this was not a great plan; it was an evil plan, and it showed that the devil had control of Judas. However, Jesus had not given up on Judas. On the night of the last supper, the Lord offered him one last chance to give his heart to God. Judas felt the call of the Holy Spirit, but he decided not to act on it, and that is when he left the last supper to make the final deal with the chief priests and lead them to Jesus.

Later that night when the temple guards roughly dragged Jesus out of the garden and down through the streets of Jerusalem, Judas knew that things were not going right. It looked as if Jesus was going to let the priests do whatever they wanted with Him. Jesus had predicted that the priests and elders would eventually crucify Him, but Judas had not really believed Him. Now he could see that everything was happening just as Jesus had said it would.

When he realized that Jesus was not going to free Himself, he became desperate and begged the priests to let Him go. "I have sinned by betraying innocent blood!" he cried with bitter tears as he threw the bag of silver coins on the floor in front of them.

However, it was too late! The deed was done. The priests were unmoved by his tears and annoyed that everyone might find out about their sneaky plans with Judas. "That is your problem!" they said rudely and sent him away. He had helped them catch Jesus, and that is all they cared about. They did not need him anymore.

Judas became desperate and begged the priests to let Jesus go.

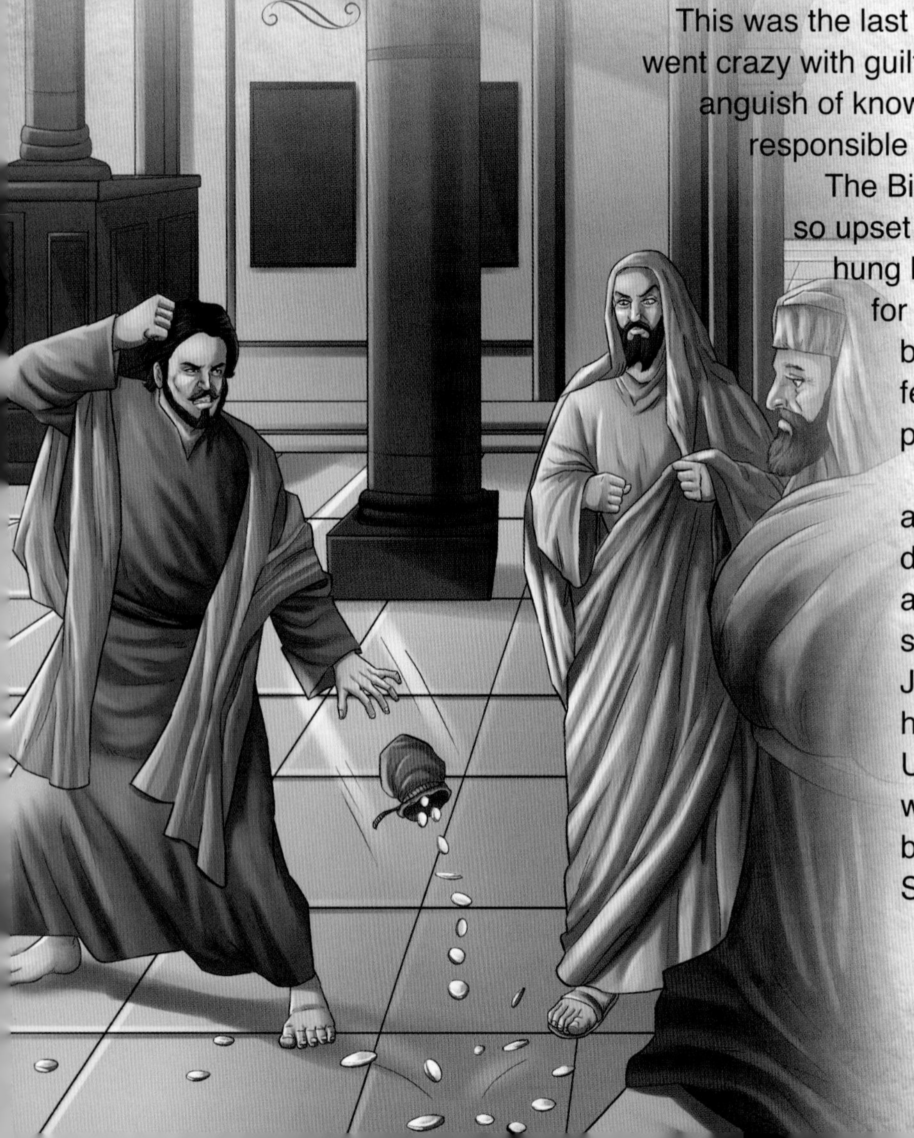

This was the last straw for Judas, and he went crazy with guilt! He could not take the anguish of knowing that he was the one responsible for Jesus' death.

The Bible says that Judas was so upset that he went out and hung himself. He was sorry for his part in the betrayal, but not truly sorry. He felt bad only because his plans had failed.

So ended the life of a man who could have done so much for Jesus and the church. If he had surrendered his life to Jesus, his story would have been very different. Unfortunately, today we remember him only because he betrayed the Son of God.

Our Prayer:

"Dear Jesus, I pray that I will never betray You, and will always be faithful."

Hidden Treasure Questions:

- ✔ How many pieces of silver did the priests give Judas for Jesus?
- ✔ What did Judas mean when he said, "I have sinned and betrayed innocent blood"?

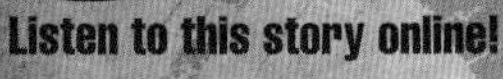

Listen to this story online!

Scan for bonus content

In Pilate's Judgment Hall

This story is taken from Matthew 27, Mark 15, Luke 23, John 18 and 19, and *The Desire of Ages*, chapter 77.

It was morning now. Jesus had been awake all night, and He was worn out. The chief priests and elders had dragged Him from one place to another as if He were a criminal. They had mocked Him, spit on Him, beat Him, and finally condemned Him to death because He claimed to be the Son of God.

Now that it was morning, the priests and elders took Jesus to see Pilate, the governor of Judea.

"Why are you bringing this Man to me?" we can imagine Pilate asking them impatiently when they arrived at his court. He was not very happy at being disturbed this early in the morning.

"If He were not an evildoer, we would not have delivered Him up to you!" the priests replied.

"What accusation do you bring against Him?" Pilate asked.

"He tells people not to pay taxes to Caesar," the priests said, "and besides this, He claims He is the Messiah, and a King."

"Then you take Him and judge Him according to your law," Pilate said.

"According to our laws He is guilty of death," said the priests, "but we're not allowed to do that. Only a Roman court can convict someone and sentence him to die."

Now that it was morning, the priests and elders took Jesus to see Pilate, the governor of Judea.

"Are You the King of the Jews?" Pilate asked Jesus.

Jesus searched Pilate's eyes. "Are you speaking for yourself about this," Jesus asked, "or did others tell you to ask Me?"

"Am I a Jew?" Pilate said. "Your own nation and the chief priests have delivered You to me. What have You done?"

"My kingdom is not of this world," Jesus answered. "If it were, My servants would fight so that I should not be delivered to the Jews."

"Are You a king, then?" Pilate asked.

"I am," Jesus replied. "For this cause I was born, and for this cause I have come into the world, that I should bear witness to the truth."

"What is truth?" Pilate stared at Jesus, and then went out again to the Jews.

"I find no fault in Him at all," he said.

When the priests heard this, they were very upset. Was Jesus going to end up going free because they couldn't convince Pilate that He was guilty? "He stirs up the people everywhere!" they shouted in desperation. "First, He did it in Galilee, and now in Judea!"

When Pilate heard that Jesus was from Galilee, he sent Him to see Herod Antipas, who happened to be in Jerusalem at the time. Herod was the ruler of the Romans in Galilee. Maybe he could make a decision about what to do with Jesus, Pilate thought. Then Pilate would not have to deal with the priests and make such a decision.

It was early morning for Herod too, but he was glad to see Jesus. He had heard much about Jesus and hoped to see Him do a miracle. However, Jesus would not answer his questions and did not perform any miracles for him. That made Herod so angry that he began cursing Jesus. He had his soldiers dress Jesus in a purple robe as a king so that they could mock Him, and then he sent Him back to Pilate.

When He arrived, Pilate gave the priests his decision. "After examining Jesus, I find no fault in Him. King Herod found no guilt either. This Man does not deserve to die; therefore, I will chastise Him and release Him."

"No," the priests shouted angrily, "condemn this Man! He deserves to die because He said He is the Son of God."

Pilate was really worried when he heard them say that and went back to talk with Jesus again. "Where are You from?" he asked, but Jesus did not answer him.

Pilate knew now that he should release Jesus.

"Why don't You say something?" Pilate demanded. "Don't You know that I have the power to crucify You and the power to release You?"

Jesus said to him, "You would have no power at all over Me if it had not been given you from above."

Pilate knew now that he should release Jesus. The priests had said that He claimed to be the Son of God, and now Jesus was telling Pilate that he had no power except what God had given him from heaven.

"I'm going to release Him," Pilate said to the priests when he went back outside again. "I find no fault in Him."

"Crucify Him! Crucify Him!" everyone kept shouting. "If you let this Man go, you are not Caesar's friend. Jesus said He is a king, and whoever makes himself a king speaks against Caesar."

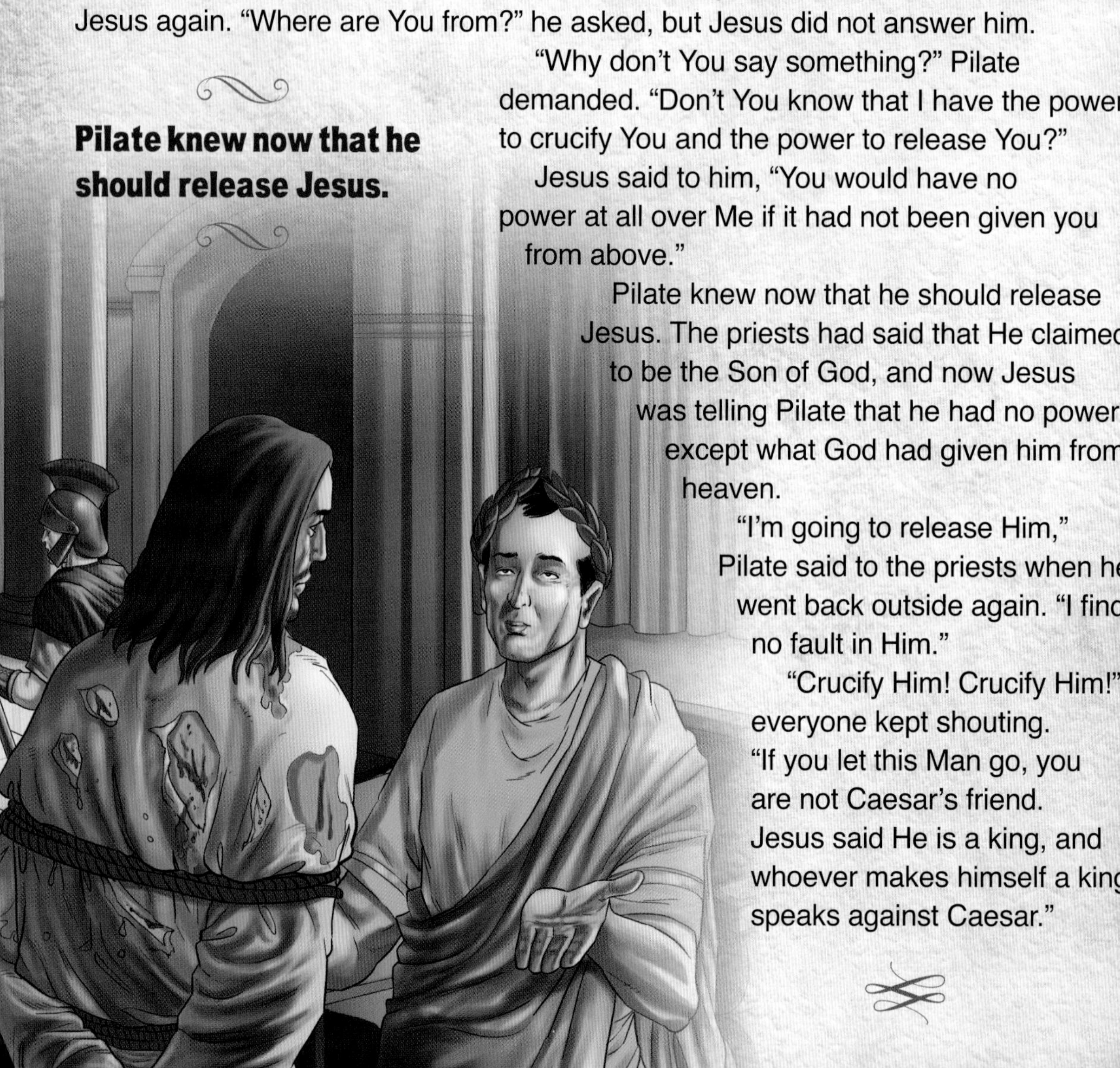

Our Prayer:

"Dear Jesus, I'm sorry You had to suffer to save me from my sins. I pray that I will always be grateful."

Hidden Treasure Questions:

- What was the name of the Judean governor when Jesus was put on trial?
- Why did King Herod want to see Jesus?

Listen to this story online!

Scan for bonus content

Crucify Him

This story is taken from Matthew 27, Mark 15, Luke 23, John 18 and 19, and *The Desire of Ages*, chapter 77.

Jesus was standing trial before Pilate for the second time since dawn, and Pilate did not know what to do. He could tell that Jesus was not guilty as the chief priests of Israel had said He was, but he wanted to please them.

While Pilate was sitting there trying to make up his mind, a servant came with an urgent message from his wife. "Have nothing to do with that just Man," she said, "for I have suffered many things this morning in a dream because of Him." This was no ordinary dream. This was a warning from God, and she knew it.

Now Pilate was really worried. He did not want to sentence an innocent man to death, much less one who was the Son of God! Then he thought of something. Every year at Passover, it was the custom to set a prisoner free. So he brought out a prisoner named Barabbas, who had been thrown into prison for murder and starting a rebellion in the city.

Satan was in that crowd making the soldiers want to spit on Jesus and slap and curse Him. Jesus was in great pain, but He never complained.

"Whom shall I release, Jesus or Barabbas?" he asked the crowds.

"Barabbas!" they shouted. "Release to us Barabbas!" The priests had stirred up the crowd to say they all wanted Barabbas instead of Jesus.

Pilate could not believe his ears. "Then what shall I do with Jesus?"

"Let Him be crucified!" the crowd screamed.

"Why? What evil has He done?" Pilate demanded. "I have found no reason to execute Him. Therefore, I will chastise Him and let Him go."

But the crowd kept shouting, "Crucify Him! Crucify Him!"

When Pilate realized he could do nothing to save Jesus, he asked for a basin of water and washed his hands. "I am innocent of the blood of this just Person!" he said.

However, the priests and all the people shouted, "His blood be on us and on our children!"

So Pilate released Barabbas to them and sent Jesus away to be scourged. Scourging was a horrible way to be whipped in Jesus' day. The whole garrison of soldiers gathered around now and began to beat Him with a whip that had little pieces of metal in it. The metal cut His skin to ribbons, making Him bleed badly.

Next, the soldiers put a purple robe on Him and a stick in His right hand. They also made a crown of twisted thorns and put it on His head. Then, kneeling in front of Him, they mocked Him. "Hail, King of the Jews!" they said as they hit Him on the head with the stick.

Satan was in that crowd making the soldiers want to spit on Jesus and slap and curse Him. Jesus was in great pain, but He never complained.

After this, the soldiers sent Him back to Pilate. When Jesus came to stand in front of the people, He was still wearing the crown of thorns. Pilate said, "Behold your King!"

"Crucify Him!" the crowds continued shouting.

"Shall I crucify your King?" Pilate said.

"We have no king but Caesar!" the crowd shouted.

At this, Pilate gave up. He wanted to save Jesus, but he was too concerned with public opinion to do the right thing. If the Jewish leaders complained to Caesar in Rome about this, he might lose his position as governor of Judea.

So Pilate turned Jesus over to the executioners to be crucified, and they led Him away. A heavy wooden cross was put on His shoulders. He was forced to carry the cross to the place of His crucifixion. However, He was so weak from loss of blood and the weight of the world's sins on Him that He collapsed right in the middle of the street.

The soldiers saw a man nearby, grabbed him, and rudely placed on his shoulders the cross.

The soldiers saw a man standing nearby, grabbed him, and rudely placed on his shoulders the cross that Christ could no longer bear. His name was Simon from Cyrene. He was probably afraid when the soldiers grabbed him out of the crowd, but what a privilege it was for him to help Jesus in His hour of need.

Then they continued on the bloody path toward Calvary, step after painful step. As they passed through the crowded streets of Jerusalem, many people mocked Jesus and made fun of Him. Some of them had been with Jesus the day of His triumphal ride into Jerusalem. They had waved palm branches and shouted, "Blessed is He who comes in the name of the Lord!" Now they were shouting, "Crucify Him!"

Others were so sad that they could hardly bear to watch Jesus being led away to die. This was the cruelest thing they had ever witnessed. How could they treat the kindest Man they had ever known this way?

Our Prayer:

"Dear Jesus, help me to be like You and to not complain."

Hidden Treasure Questions:

- ✔ Who sent a message to Pilate telling him not to condemn Jesus?
- ✔ What did Pilate do to show everyone that he was innocent of Jesus' blood?

Listen to this story online!

Scan for bonus content

Calvary

This story is taken from Matthew 27, Mark 15, Luke 23, John 19, and *The Desire of Ages*, chapters 78 and 79.

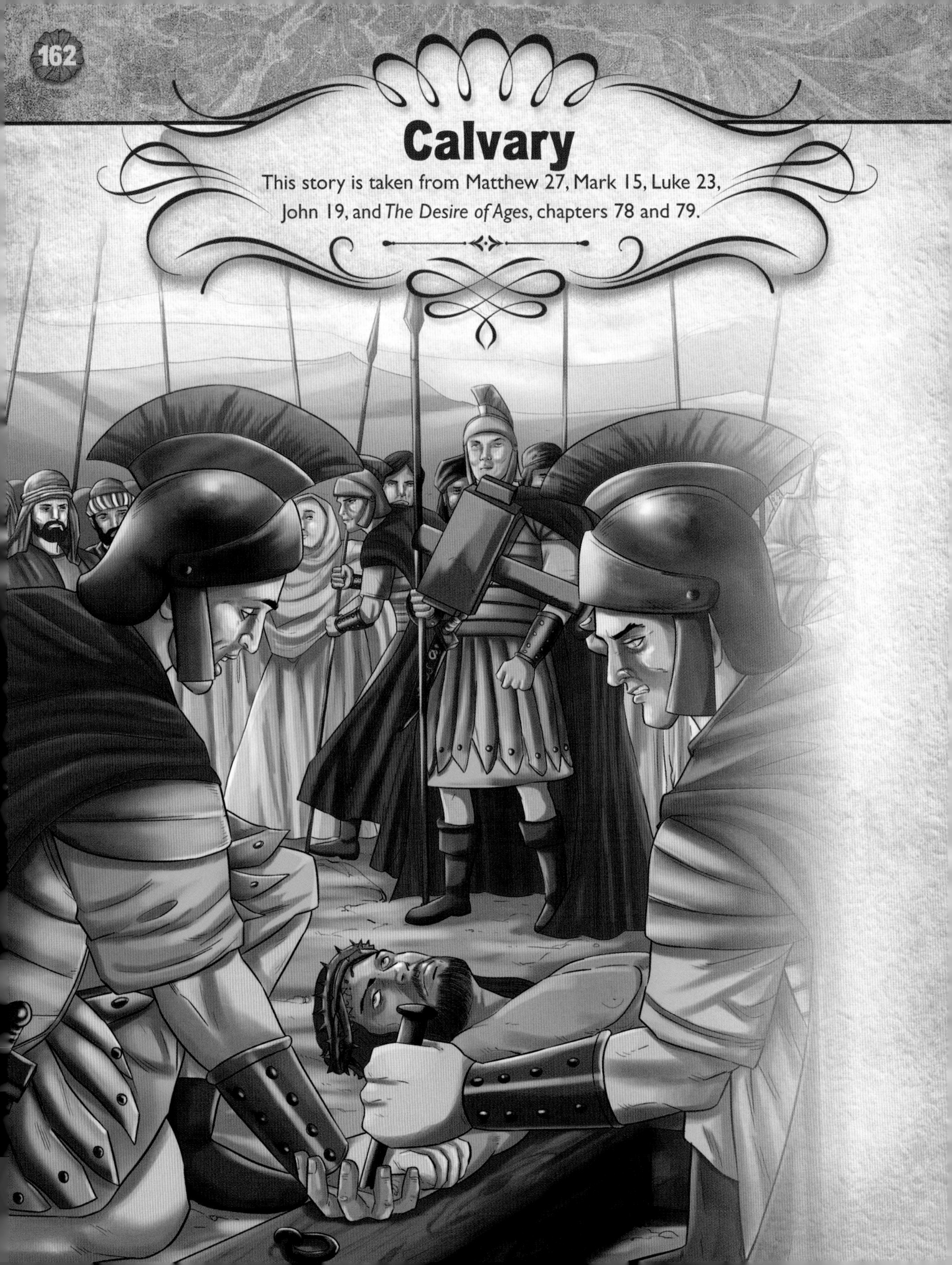

What a terrible day this was turning out to be! Jesus was on the hill of Golgotha about to be crucified. Crucifixion was the cruelest death known to man. Already that morning He had been interrogated at least three times by the priests and scribes, and another three times by the Romans. He had been severely beaten and then scourged, and finally a crown of sharp thorns had been jammed on His head.

It was nine o'clock when the Roman soldiers threw Jesus' cross on the ground and laid Him on it. Then they hammered spikes through His hands and feet to the crossbeams and lifted the cross to drop it into a hole in the ground. That jolt sent shock waves of pain through Jesus' body, but He did not complain. It must have been excruciating, and yet He prayed for His executioners, "Father, forgive them, for they do not know what they do."

They hammered spikes through His hands and feet to the crossbeams and lifted the cross to drop it into a hole in the ground.

This was no ordinary execution, but neither the Romans nor the Jews realized it. Jesus had battled with Satan in the garden the night before. He did not want to die on the cross, but He knew that if He wanted to save the human race, He must go through with the plan that He and the Father had made long ago! He knew that the hope of every man and woman, every boy and girl depended on Him. Though it would cost Him everything, He must pay the price for everyone who wished to accept His offer of salvation.

So they crucified Him between two thieves on the hill of Calvary. Just as the prophecies of Scripture had predicted, Jesus was executed with criminals.

His executioners put a sign written in Hebrew, Greek, and Latin on the cross that said: JESUS OF NAZARETH, THE KING OF THE JEWS. The wicked, self-righteous priests complained about the words Pilate had put on the sign. "He is not our king!" they argued, but Pilate was so angry with the priests for pushing him to crucify Jesus that he just said, "What I have written, I have written!"

As Jesus hung on the cross, He suffered more than we can imagine. Some of the Romans must have felt sorry for Him because one of them offered Him some wine to drink mixed with a drug called gall, but Jesus would not take it. He wanted His mind to be clear to face the temptations that Satan was sure to bring Him while He was on the cross.

All morning people who were passing by on the road made fun of Jesus. "You said You could destroy the temple and build it in three days," they laughed. "If You have that much power, save Yourself! If You are the Son of God, come down from the cross."

The priests, the scribes, and the elders came out to mock Him too. "He saved others, but He cannot save Himself! If He is the King of Israel, the Chosen One of God, let Him now come down from the cross, and we will believe Him! He trusted in God! Let God deliver Him, if He can. After all, He said, 'I am the Son of God.'"

Jesus was touched by the thief's testimony. "You will be with Me in paradise," He said. "I can promise you that today."

Most of the people around the cross were pointing at Jesus and mocking Him. The soldiers mocked Him too, and even one of the thieves beside Jesus cursed Him. "If You are the Christ, save Yourself and us!" he said scornfully.

But the other thief scolded him. "Don't you fear God?" he demanded. "You are under the same condemnation as He is! We did wrong, and we deserve to be crucified! We are being punished because we are criminals, but this Man has done nothing wrong."

Then he said to Jesus, "Lord, remember me when You come into Your kingdom."

Jesus was touched by the thief's testimony. "You will be with Me in paradise," He said. "I can promise you that today."

As He looked down from the cross that day, Jesus spotted His mother and His disciple John. "Woman, behold your son," he said, looking at John, and then, "John, behold your mother." Jesus wanted John to take care of His mother for Him when He was gone, and that is exactly what John did. From that day forward, she went to live in his home.

About noon, a strange darkness came over the land, settling on Jerusalem, and especially Golgotha. It surrounded the cross of Jesus as if to hide Him from the shame of being crucified.

Those who had been scoffing at Jesus all morning were silent now. Priests, scribes, Roman soldiers, and the mob were afraid of what was coming. Lightning flashed now and then, revealing Jesus in the darkness. Some of the people huddling on the hill of Calvary now whispered that Jesus would come down from the cross. Others attempted to grope their way back to the city wailing as if their last day of life had come.

Then about three o'clock in the afternoon the darkness lifted from the city and Golgotha, but it still surrounded the cross.

Suddenly Jesus cried out, "Eli, Eli, lama sabachthani?" or, in other words, "My God, My God, why have You forsaken Me?"

Some who were standing nearby said, "He must be calling for Elijah!"

One of the soldiers felt sorry for Jesus because He looked so thirsty. He took a sponge and filled it with sour wine, then put it on a long stick and offered Jesus a drink with it.

However, others were not so compassionate. "Leave Him alone," they said. "Let's see if Elijah will come to save Him."

But Jesus now had peace in His heart. He knew He had done what He came to do in this world. The battle against Satan and sin had been won.

He had shown the Father's infinite love to the whole universe, and He must die now to prove it.

"It is finished!" Jesus cried out again with a loud voice, as a light from heaven shone on His face. "Father, into Thy hands I commend My spirit!" Then He died.

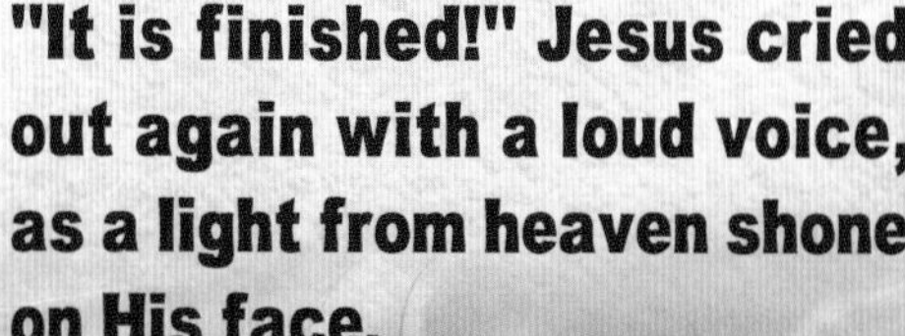
"It is finished!" Jesus cried out again with a loud voice, as a light from heaven shone on His face.

At that moment, an earthquake shook Golgotha and the city of Jerusalem. Then an unseen hand tore the curtain in the temple from top to bottom, opening up the Most Holy Place for all to see. The priest who was getting ready to offer the evening sacrifice dropped his knife, and the lamb to be sacrificed ran away. This was to show that there was no need for sacrifices in this temple anymore. The Lamb of God had just given His life for the world.

Oh wonderful,wonderful Jesus who gave His life for you and me. He died between two sinners that everyone might be offered life eternal. To receive this gift all you have to do is accept it. Won't you ask Him to come into your life today?

"Dear Jesus, thank You so much for Your sacrifice.
How can I ever repay You?"

Hidden Treasure Questions:

- ✔ What time of day was Jesus crucified?
- ✔ Whom did Jesus ask to take care of His mother?

Listen to this story online!

Scan for bonus content

In Joseph's Tomb

This story is taken from Matthew 27, Mark 15, Luke 23, John 19, and *The Desire of Ages*, chapter 80.

It was a very sad day! Jesus had just died on the cross! How could this happen? The Son of God dead! How was that possible? Jesus had tried very hard to explain that this terrible, but necessary, event was going to happen. However, even His own disciples had refused to listen.

The Holy Scriptures had foretold that this would happen. Somehow when the disciples and others read that part of Scripture, they were blinded to its meaning. When the time had come, Jesus knew that He must give up His life, and He did it willingly. As Isaiah the prophet said, "He was wounded for our transgressions. . . . By His stripes we are healed" (Isaiah 53:5).

The two thieves on either side of Jesus were not dead yet, and that was a big problem for the chief priests. Evening was coming fast. It was almost time for the Sabbath to begin. The Passover celebration was this weekend, and the Jewish leaders could not have the bodies of these three men hanging on crosses during the Sabbath hours. Such a thing would defile the city and the whole celebration of the Passover Feast.

Joseph carefully wrapped Jesus' body in a clean linen cloth and laid Him in the tomb. Then a large stone was rolled across the entrance.

What a bunch of hypocrites! These wicked priests had killed the spotless Son of God. Now they were worried about His dead body defiling the Sabbath and the Passover Feast to come!

Therefore, sometime near sunset they ordered that the legs of Jesus and the two thieves be broken so that they would die before the Sabbath began. The only way for a victim on a cross to stay alive was to push down on the nails in their feet so they could breathe. When the legs were broken, the person would then suffocate.

So that is what the Roman soldiers did to the thieves, and within a short time, they were dead. However, when they came to Jesus, they found Him already dead. To make sure, one of the soldiers pushed his spear into Jesus' side, and out came two streams, one of water and the other blood.

Now the body of Christ had to be taken care of. The disciples had no money for burial supplies and no place to put His body. Tombs were very expensive in those days, and only the wealthy could afford them.

At this time, some very rich followers of Jesus came forward to help with the burial. Nicodemus and Joseph of Arimathea had been hesitant to stand up for Jesus publicly while He was alive, but now they realized that they must give their all to Jesus.

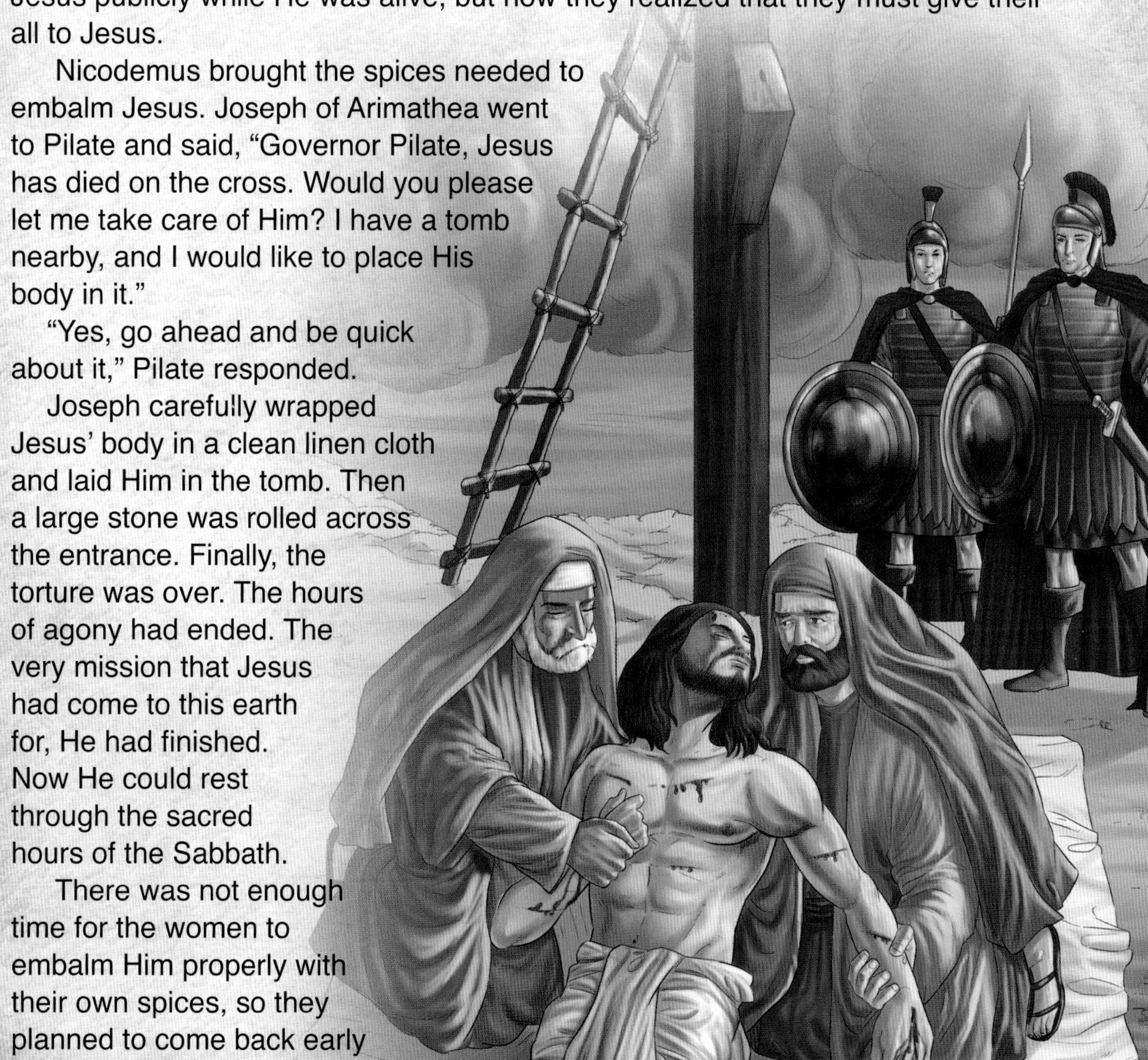

Nicodemus brought the spices needed to embalm Jesus. Joseph of Arimathea went to Pilate and said, "Governor Pilate, Jesus has died on the cross. Would you please let me take care of Him? I have a tomb nearby, and I would like to place His body in it."

"Yes, go ahead and be quick about it," Pilate responded.

Joseph carefully wrapped Jesus' body in a clean linen cloth and laid Him in the tomb. Then a large stone was rolled across the entrance. Finally, the torture was over. The hours of agony had ended. The very mission that Jesus had come to this earth for, He had finished. Now He could rest through the sacred hours of the Sabbath.

There was not enough time for the women to embalm Him properly with their own spices, so they planned to come back early Sunday morning.

All that evening and the following Sabbath day, the disciples hid out of sight in the upper room. They were very frightened that the temple priests might now come looking for them and kill them.

Meanwhile, on Sabbath afternoon the chief priests visited Pilate to convince him that he needed to post a guard around the tomb of Jesus. "Sir, we remember while He was still alive how that deceiver said, 'After three days, I will rise again.' Therefore, command that the tomb be made secure until the third day, or His disciples might come by night and steal Him away and say to the people, 'He has risen from the dead.'"

On Sabbath afternoon the chief priests visited Pilate to convince him that he needed to post a guard around the tomb of Jesus.

Pilate agreed and said, "Go make it as secure as possible. I will send 100 soldiers with you to be sure no one touches the body. Also, I will have it sealed. If anyone breaks that seal, they will be put to death."

Everything that could be done was done. The priests took every precaution to keep Jesus in the grave. Pilate made it seemingly impossible for anything or anyone to move the body of Jesus.

However, the priests, rulers, and even Roman governors are no match for God. Remember, Jesus said, "With God all things are possible." In just a few hours, the thing they feared most would happen, and then they would know that Jesus was indeed the Son of God and the Savior of the world.

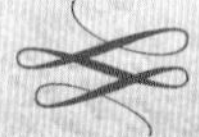

Our Prayer:

"Dear Jesus, thank You for taking the penalty for my sins."

Hidden Treasure Questions:

- ✔ Who came to offer his own tomb to bury Jesus properly?
- ✔ Why did the chief priests ask Pilate to put soldiers around Jesus' tomb?

Listen to this story online!

Scan for bonus content

Jesus' Resurrection

This story is taken from Matthew 28, Mark 15, Luke 24, John 20 and *The Desire of Ages*, chapter 81.

It was early morning. The sun was not yet up to chase the shadows of the night away. Dew still covered the wild rose vines growing along the path leading to the tomb where Jesus had been laid to rest. Day was coming. The little crickets had finally stopped chirping, and nighthawks no longer swooped in the skies above.

Gathered around Jesus' tomb were many of Pilate's best Roman soldiers. Some were standing guard at the door of the tomb; others were sitting on the ground. The Jewish priests had sent them to the tomb under Pilate's orders because they thought that the disciples might try to take the body of Jesus. However, everything was quiet, and it looked as if it would be an uneventful day

Suddenly the ground began to shake. They probably thought that this was just another earthquake like the one on Friday when Jesus had died on the cross.

But this time it was different. The soldiers staggered to their feet as the rumbling grew louder. Suddenly a bright flash of light came down from the sky, lighting up the tomb and everyone around it. The soldiers didn't know what it was for sure, but they knew that it must be some kind of a supernatural being, because the form of a majestic angel appeared. His face was like lightning, and his robe of light was as white as snow!

With a sweep of his hand, the angel brushed aside the giant stone at the entrance of the tomb as if it were a pebble. "Son of God, come out!" the angel announced in trumpetlike tones. "Your Father calls You!"

Gathered around Jesus' tomb were many of Pilate's best Roman soldiers.

Other angels had come to the tomb that morning to witness the most exciting day in

With a sweep of his hand, the angel brushed aside the giant stone at the entrance of the tomb as if it were a pebble.

heaven since Jesus had come to earth as a baby. Now, if the angels sang in the hills surrounding Bethlehem to announce the birth of Jesus, it seems only right that they would come and sing to announce His resurrection.

And that's exactly what they did! At the moment of Jesus' resurrection, a choir of angels suddenly burst into singing to welcome Him from the grave! Can you imagine the glorious song they sang? It was like no song you have ever heard.

In the next instant Jesus was at the open doorway to the tomb. No longer was He dressed in the clothes of a poor man, but He was in the glorious robes of heaven. "I am the resurrection and the life!" He announced to the listening soldiers and the world. With this announcement Jesus gave hope to everyone who believes in Him. In this life we may face the sorrow of someone we love dying. But because Jesus rose from the grave, we have hope of one day seeing them again.

By now the soldiers had all fallen to the ground to shield their faces from His glory. Daring and cruel as they had been to beat Him nearly to death on Friday, they now became like dead men, hiding their faces from the majestic One they had crucified.

"I am the resurrection and the life!" Jesus announced to the listening soldiers and the world.

And then the moment was gone just as quickly as it had come. When the glorious light of Jesus and the angels died away, the soldiers scrambled to their feet and hurried to Jerusalem. The news awoke the priests from their beds, and they learned the whole story of the bright angel and the resurrection of Jesus from the dead.

The priests panicked at the news of this story. If what the soldiers said was true, then they had indeed crucified the Messiah, the King of kings and Lord of lords! And if that was possible, then they would be considered enemies of heaven. If the people in Jerusalem found out, they would tear these priests from their positions of power and probably even stone them to death. The priests could not let that happen.

So it was that the priests created their own story, instructing the soldiers to tell everyone a lie. They said, "Just say that Jesus' disciples came by night to steal His body while the soldiers slept."

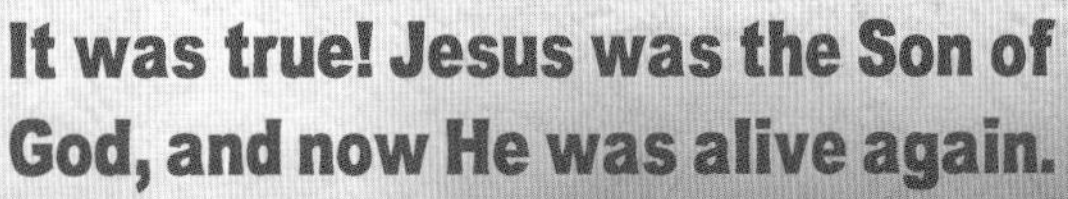

Of course, the soldiers were afraid to tell such a story because any soldier caught sleeping at his post of duty would be executed. But the priests bribed the soldiers with money and promised to settle the whole issue with Pilate to keep them out of trouble.

However, the real story had already gotten to Pilate, and when he heard the details he turned pale. So, it was true! Jesus was the Son of God, and now He was alive again. Pilate probably never slept well again after that, thinking of the part he played in Jesus' cruel crucifixion.

It was true! Jesus was the Son of God, and now He was alive again.

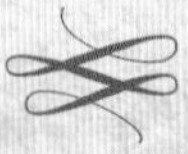

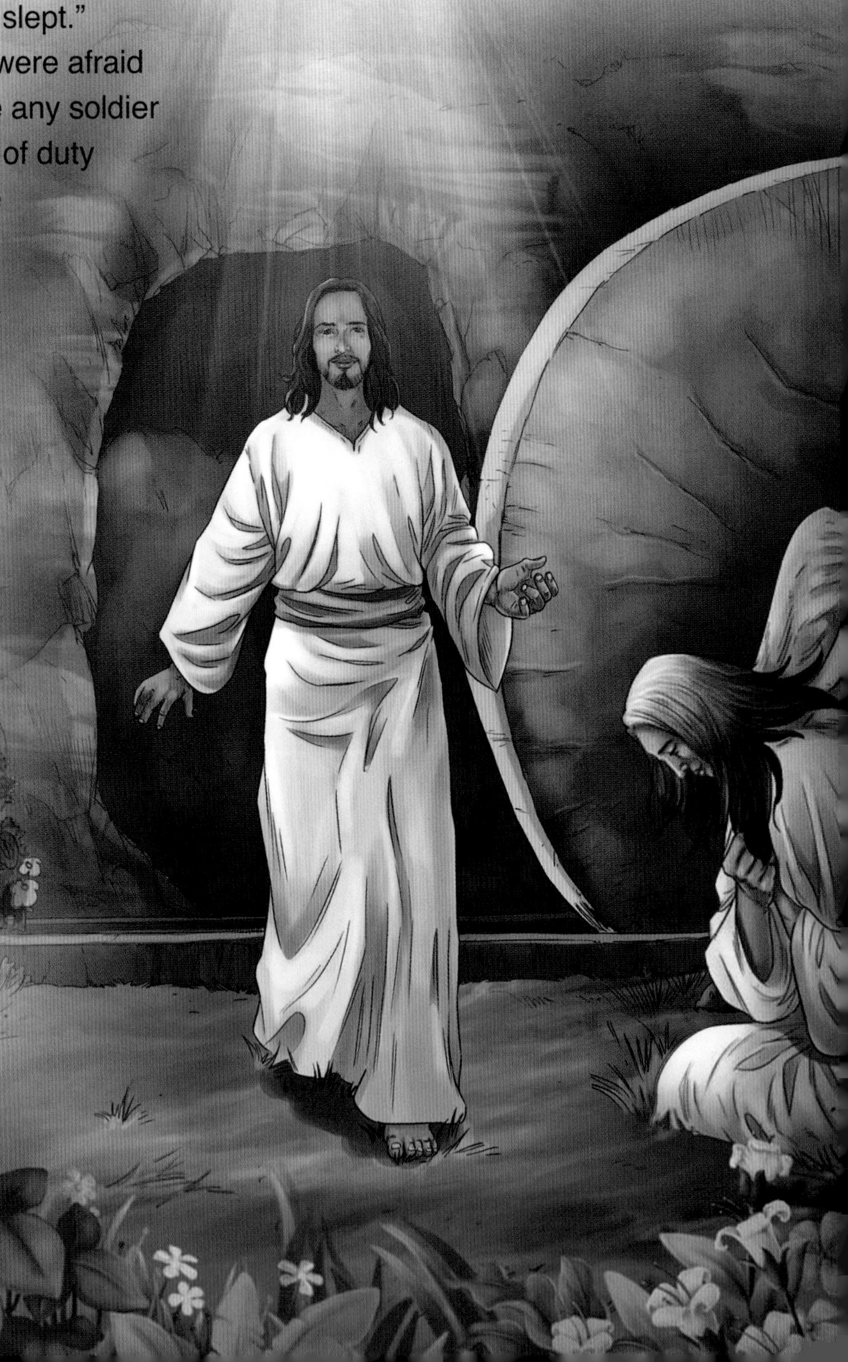

Our Prayer:

"Thank You, Jesus, for the hope of life after death. Thank You for the promise that all those we love can someday be resurrected to live with You forever in heaven."

Hidden Treasure Questions:

- ✔ What song do you think the angels sang at Jesus' resurrection?
- ✔ What do you think was going through Pilate's mind when he heard that Jesus had risen?

Listen to this story online!

Scan for bonus content

An Empty Tomb

This story is taken from Matthew 28, Mark 16, Luke 24, John 20, and *The Desire of Ages,* chapter 82.

The dawn had nearly come. Turtledoves cooed their early morning love songs in the olive trees along the Kidron Valley. Any moment now, the sun would rise from behind Jerusalem's hills to the east.

The gates of the city had just been opened, and several women were now on their way to Jesus' tomb to anoint His body with spices and ointments. They had not been able to finish the job on Friday when they laid Jesus in the tomb, because the Sabbath was about to begin.

Now they wondered how they were going to get inside the tomb to anoint the body of Jesus. The stone to the tomb was too heavy for them to move.

Mary Magdalene reached the tomb first. To her surprise, the stone had already been rolled away! There had been 100 soldiers guarding the tomb the night before, but now there was no one in sight. Where were they? The tomb was empty. Had they moved the body of Jesus to another tomb?

Mary Magdalene hurried off to the city to tell the disciples that the tomb was empty. Meanwhile, the other women reached the tomb and realized that they were not alone.

An angel was sitting on the stone that had been rolled away from the tomb, his clothes still shining with the light of heaven. The women were surprised and turned away in fear.

"Don't be afraid," said the angel. "Why are you looking for the living among the dead? I know that you are looking for Jesus, who was crucified. He is not here; He is risen, as He said. Come; see the place where the Lord lay."

The women bent down to look into the tomb and saw another angel in shining clothes. "Go quickly and tell His disciples," the angel told them. "He is risen from the dead and is going ahead of you into Galilee. You will see Him there."

The women hurried away, with fear and great joy, to share the good news with the disciples. "He is risen!" they kept telling one another.

Meanwhile, Mary had returned with Peter and John to find that the tomb was indeed empty. The two disciples did not yet understand everything that they saw, but they did remember that Jesus had said He would arise from the dead. Now they hurried off to Jerusalem, very excited about what they had found.

Mary stayed near the tomb. She had not been with the other women when the angel told them that Jesus was risen. Tears blinded her eyes as she thought about all that Jesus had done to help her. Now He was gone, and they couldn't find out where they had taken His body.

She went to the tomb and looked inside again. Two men in white were sitting in the place

"Don't be afraid," said the angel. "Why are you looking for the living among the dead?"

where Jesus had lain. "Why are you crying?" they asked her.

"Because they have taken my Lord away, and I don't know where they have put Him," she said and then quickly turned away. She was so upset that she did not realize that these men were angels who had come to encourage her.

Through her tears, she noticed another man standing nearby. "Why are you crying?" the stranger asked kindly. "Who are you are looking for?"

She thought the man must be the gardener. "If you have carried Him away, sir, tell me where you have put Him. I would like to finish anointing His body for burial."

In an instant, she knew that this was Jesus..."Teacher!" she cried out.

Then Jesus called her name. "Mary!"

In an instant, she knew that this was Jesus, the crucified and risen Savior. "Teacher!" she cried out and fell at His feet to worship Him.

"I cannot stay longer," Jesus told Mary. "Go now and tell the disciples that I must go see My Father and your Father, who is in heaven."

"I have seen the Lord!" Mary exclaimed again and again as she raced off to tell everyone the good news. "He has risen from the dead!"

That was indeed the best news the world would ever hear. The Son of God had risen from the tomb, and all those who trust in Him can now have the hope of eternal life.

One day soon, Jesus will come again, and everyone who helped kill Him will see who Jesus really is. Those who tried to keep Him in the grave will see that He is Lord of heaven and earth, the God of all creation. He is the resurrection and the life!

Our Prayer:

"Lord, thank You that I can help spread the good news of Jesus' resurrection."

Hidden Treasure Questions:

- ✔ Why was Jesus' death so hard for Mary Magdalene?
- ✔ How many angels were at the tomb of Jesus to encourage the disciples?

Listen to this story online!

Scan for bonus content

The Walk to Emmaus

This story is taken from Luke 24 and
The Desire of Ages, chapters 83 and 84.

Everybody was talking about the resurrection of Jesus. According to Mary Magdalene and several others, He was alive! The Roman soldiers were spreading a rumor that Jesus was not alive. They said, "Jesus' body was stolen from the tomb by His disciples." But everyone knew that this was a lie that the priests had started.

Then there was a very large group of people in Jerusalem that weekend who surprised everyone who saw them. They were those who had been raised from the dead when Christ arose. Those people went around saying, "Jesus has risen from the dead, and He raised us also."

Now, traveling on the road from Jerusalem to Emmaus that very same afternoon were Cleopas and another follower of Jesus. They were very discouraged about the death of Jesus. Although the stories of Jesus' resurrection seemed real enough, they had not seen Him themselves.

While they were walking along and discussing the events

of the weekend, a stranger joined them on the road. It was Jesus, but these two men were so preoccupied with their sadness over Jesus' death that they did not recognize Him.

"What kind of conversation is this that you are having with each other as you walk?" Jesus asked them.

"Are You the only stranger in Jerusalem who doesn't know the things that have happened there these past few days?" Cleopas responded in surprise.

"What things?" Jesus asked.

"The things concerning Jesus of Nazareth, who was a Prophet, mighty in deed and word before God and all the people, and how the chief priests and our rulers delivered Him to be condemned to death, and crucified Him," Cleopas added. "But we were hoping that it was He who was going to redeem Israel. Today is the third day since these things have happened. And when certain women of our company arrived at the tomb early, they were astonished because they did not find His body. They told us that they had seen a vision of angels who said He was alive. Some who were with us went to the tomb and found it just as the women had said, but we did not actually see Him ourselves."

Jesus understood that His crucifixion and death had been a hard time for everyone. However, He had warned them that His death was coming, and besides, the Scriptures had prophesied it.

"Oh, foolish ones and slow of heart to believe in all that the prophets have spoken!' Jesus said. "Is it not true that Christ should have suffered these things?"

"Oh, foolish ones and slow of heart to believe in all that the prophets have spoken!" Jesus said.

He began to quote Moses and the prophets, explaining to them all the Scriptures that pointed to Himself as the Messiah. It must have been a wonderful Bible study. By the time they had reached the village of Emmaus, eight miles from Jerusalem, the disciples were more encouraged.

As they drew near their house, Jesus acted as though He would go farther on the road, but they urged Him to stay with them for a meal and the night.

As they sat down for the meal, Jesus blessed the bread and broke it, just as He had always done when He was with His disciples. Suddenly, the eyes of these men were opened. No sooner had they recognized Him than He disappeared from their sight.

They were so excited that they jumped up from the unfinished meal and hurried all the way back to Jerusalem to tell the other disciples what they had seen. "Did not our hearts burn within us while He talked with us on the road, and while He opened the Scriptures to us?" they said to each other.

In Jerusalem, they found a large group of disciples gathered together in the upper room saying that Jesus had appeared to Peter. That was very exciting news, especially for Peter, since he had denied even knowing Jesus the morning of the crucifixion.

Jesus blessed the bread and broke it. Suddenly, the eyes of these men were opened.

However, when Cleopas and his friend shared their story about how Jesus quoted Scripture and then broke bread with them, the group must have been very excited! Then, as if things could not get any more exciting, Jesus Himself suddenly appeared among them.

"Peace to you," He said kindly, but many were terrified. They thought He was a ghost.

"Why are you afraid?" He asked them. "Look at My hands and My feet. It's Me. Touch Me and see, because a ghost doesn't have skin and bones such as I have."

Jesus asked for some food to prove that He was not a ghost. So they brought Him something to eat. As He ate the food, He encouraged them and reminded them of their mission to the world. "As the Father has sent Me," He said, "I also send you."

Our Prayer:

"Dear Jesus, I'm so excited that You have risen from the dead and that You are alive today!"

Hidden Treasure Questions:

- ✔ Which town were the two disciples walking to when Jesus joined them?
- ✔ How many miles did the two disciples walk that day?

Listen to this story online!

Scan for bonus content

Feed My Sheep

This story is taken from Matthew 28, John 21, and *The Desire of Ages*, chapters 84-87.

Jesus was no longer dead! He had risen just as He had said He would, and many people had seen Him. Some doubted that it had actually happened, though, and Thomas, His own disciple, was one of them. For some reason, he had not been in the upper room when Jesus came to visit everybody, and now he refused to believe that Jesus had risen.

"Unless I see in His hands the print of the nails, I will not believe," Thomas said. He was probably jealous of the others, and maybe a little hurt that Jesus had not included him in the surprise visits.

Jesus knew Thomas well, and it was to help his faith grow that Jesus waited until eight days later to show up again. "Peace to you!" He said to Thomas, getting right to the point. "Reach your finger here and look at My hands; and reach your hand here, and put it into My side. Because you have seen Me, you have believed. Blessed are those who have not seen Me and yet have believed."

Thomas was quite upset, but this time out of shame. "My Lord and my God!" he said and bowed at Jesus' feet. He knew that he should not have doubted Jesus, and he was sorry now.

A little while later, Jesus appeared to a group of disciples who had gone back to Galilee to do a little fishing. Peter, James, and John were there, along with several others. This is how it happened.

Early one morning after the disciples had been out on the lake fishing all night, Jesus appeared to them on the shore. "Children, have you any food?" He called in His fatherly way.

"No!" they replied, not knowing it was Jesus.

"Cast the net on the right side of the boat, and you will find some!" He said, and when they did as He asked, the net quickly filled with fish. In fact, they were not able to pull the net in because there were so many fish.

"It is the Lord!" Peter suddenly shouted and jumped into the water to swim ashore. When they all got to the beach, they found a fire already lit and fish roasting on the coals.

The disciples were so happy to see Jesus! They were excited about the fish, too! This miracle was very similar to the one Jesus had done for them when He first called them to be His disciples at the lake.

It was to help Thomas' faith grow that Jesus waited until eight days later to show up again. "Peace to you!" He said to Thomas, getting right to the point.

Now Jesus broke bread and ate fish with them one last time. This was the third time that Jesus had shown Himself to His disciples as a group since He had risen from the dead.

After they had eaten breakfast, Jesus asked Peter, "Simon, son of Jonah, do you love Me more than these?" and He looked around at all the disciples.

Peter said to Him,"Yes, Lord, You know that I love You."

Peter said to Him, “Yes, Lord; You know that I love You.”

“Feed My lambs,” Jesus said.

A second time, Jesus asked him, “Simon, son of Jonah, do you love Me?”

“Yes, Lord, You know that I love You.” Peter knew that he had done wrong in denying Jesus on the night of His trial, but it still hurt to think that Jesus could not trust him.

“Tend My sheep,” Jesus replied.

A third time, Jesus asked the same question, and a third time Peter tried to reassure Jesus that he did love Him. “Lord, You know all things! You know that I love You!” Peter wanted to cry because Jesus had asked him the same question three times.

“Feed My sheep,” He told Peter. Then He opened a window into the future to let Peter know what was going to happen. “When you were younger, you dressed yourself and walked where you wished. But when you are old, you will stretch out your

hands and another will carry you where you do not wish to go."

Jesus wanted Peter to know how much it was going to cost to be His follower, and that someday he would be crucified as Jesus had been.

During the 40 days following His resurrection, Jesus appeared to many of the disciples. The Roman soldiers had been the first to see Him, along with Mary Magdalene. Then He appeared to Cleopas and his friend on the way to Emmaus. He also appeared to the disciples as a group several times, to Thomas specifically, to James, and finally to about 500 of His followers in Galilee.

"You are witnesses of all that you have seen Me do," Jesus told His disciples, "but wait in the city of Jerusalem until you are given power from on high."

Just a few days after Jesus went back to heaven, the disciples would receive the Holy Spirit, and then they would go to the world to be missionaries for Jesus! Most of them would travel to foreign countries. In Jesus' name, they would cast out demons. They would speak with new tongues. They would take up serpents, and if they drank anything deadly, it would not hurt them. They would lay hands on the sick to heal them. Most would eventually die as martyrs for the gospel.

Near the end of 40 days, Jesus took the 11 disciples with Him to the Mount of Olives. There He said His final goodbyes. It must have been a very emotional day for all of them. Most of these disciples had been with Jesus for more than three years now. They had seen and experienced so much with Him. They had watched Him heal countless people who were blind, deaf, and lame. They had seen Him turn water into grape juice, multiply loaves and fish, walk on water, and raise the dead. They had seen Him battle the Pharisees and temple teachers, and always He came out the winner.

Now they must part. Jesus' last command to His disciples was, "Go therefore and make disciples of all the nations, baptizing them in the name of the Father, and of the Son, and of the Holy Spirit, teaching them to observe all things that I have commanded you; and lo, I am with you always, even to the end of the age."

While He was talking to them, He lifted His hands to bless them. As He blessed them, He began to ascend and was carried up into heaven. The disciples strained their eyes to catch one last glimpse of Jesus. When they could not see Him anymore, two men in white suddenly appeared.

As Jesus blessed them, He began to ascend and was carried up into heaven.

"Men of Galilee," they said, "why do you stand gazing up into heaven? This same Jesus, who was taken up from you into heaven, will so come in like manner as you saw Him go into heaven."

The disciples knew that it was true. Jesus had said that He would come, and now the angels had said it, too. Excitedly, they hurried back to Jerusalem to wait to see what God would do for them through His Holy Spirit.

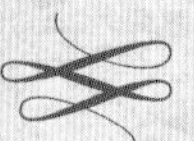

Our Prayer:

"Dear Father, thank You so much for sending Your Son to earth. We hope to see Him soon."

Hidden Treasure Questions:

- Who said he wouldn't believe that Jesus had risen until he saw the nail prints in His hands?
- What miracle did Jesus perform for His disciples while they were fishing on Lake Galilee?

Listen to this story online!

Scan for bonus content